BTEC FIRST
Principles of Applied Science

Study & Exam Practice

This book is for anyone doing **BTEC Level 2
First Award in Principles of Applied Science**.
It covers the examined unit of the course — **Unit 1**.

All the **important topics** are explained in a clear, straightforward
way to help you get all the marks you can in the exam.

It's full of **useful practice questions** to help you get to grips with
the essential science you'll need for the exams.

What CGP is all about

Our sole aim here at CGP is to produce the highest
quality books — carefully written, immaculately presented
and dangerously close to being funny.

Then we work our socks off to get them
out to you — at the cheapest possible prices.

Published by CGP

Editors:
Katherine Craig, Emma Elder, Helena Hayes, Jane Sawers, Camilla Simson,
Megan Tyler, Karen Wells.

Contributors:
Paddy Gannon

ISBN: 978 1 84762 870 1

With thanks to Rosie McCurrie and Sarah Williams for the proofreading.

With thanks to Katie Braid, Tom Davies, Rebecca Harvey, John Myers and Gary Talbot for
the reviewing.

With thanks to Laura Collar and Jan Greenway for the copyright research.

Pages 64 and 66 contain public sector information published by the Health and Safety
Executive and licensed under the Open Government Licence v1.0.

Groovy website: www.cgpbooks.co.uk

Printed by Elanders Ltd, Newcastle upon Tyne.
Jolly bits of clipart from CorelDRAW®

Based on the classic CGP style created by Richard Parsons.

Contents

Exam Tips

This book is for anyone studying BTEC First Award in Principles of Applied Science course.

Here is What Will Happen...

There are four units in this course.

Unit 1	For Unit 1, you'll have to do an exam.
Unit 2	
Unit 3	Units 2, 3 and 4 will be assessed by your teacher. Your teacher will set you assignments.
Unit 4	

Unit 1 is worth 25% of the total marks.

How to Use This Book

This book is to help you with the Unit 1 exam.

1) The revision pages have all the facts you need to learn.
   - Read a page.
   - Cover it up.
   - Scribble down what you remember.
   - Do this until you can write down all the key points on the page.

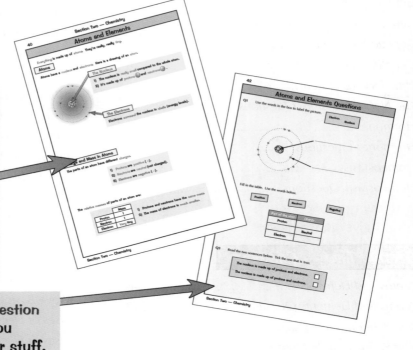

2) Now use the question pages to test you really know your stuff.

Top Exam Tips

1) Make sure you read all the information given to you in the question.
2) Look at the number of marks on offer to give you an idea of how much to write.
3) If you are asked to calculate something, make sure you show your working.
4) Make sure you understand what the question is asking you to do. Take a look at the guide on the next page for some handy tips.

Exam Tips

Types of Exam Question

Certain words in an exam question tell you what to do. It's a good idea to learn what these words mean. Then they won't be able to trip you up.

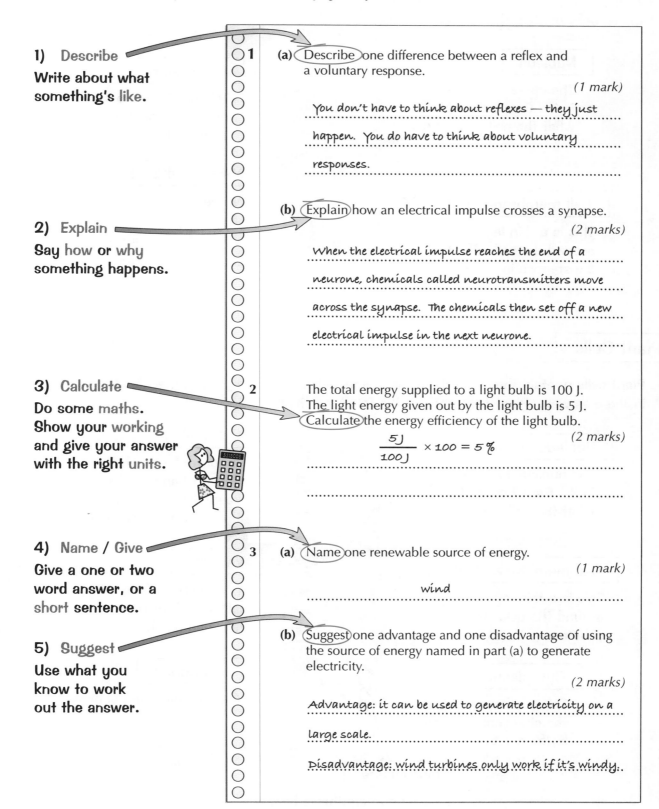

1) **Describe**

Write about what something's like.

2) **Explain**

Say how or why something happens.

3) **Calculate**

Do some maths. Show your working and give your answer with the right units.

4) **Name / Give**

Give a one or two word answer, or a short sentence.

5) **Suggest**

Use what you know to work out the answer.

1 (a) Describe one difference between a reflex and a voluntary response.

(1 mark)

You don't have to think about reflexes — they just happen. You do have to think about voluntary responses.

(b) Explain how an electrical impulse crosses a synapse.

(2 marks)

When the electrical impulse reaches the end of a neurone, chemicals called neurotransmitters move across the synapse. The chemicals then set off a new electrical impulse in the next neurone.

2 The total energy supplied to a light bulb is 100 J. The light energy given out by the light bulb is 5 J. Calculate the energy efficiency of the light bulb.

(2 marks)

$$\frac{5\ J}{100\ J} \times 100 = 5\ \%$$

3 (a) Name one renewable source of energy.

(1 mark)

wind

(b) Suggest one advantage and one disadvantage of using the source of energy named in part (a) to generate electricity.

(2 marks)

Advantage: it can be used to generate electricity on a large scale.

Disadvantage: wind turbines only work if it's windy.

Cells, Tissues and Organs

All living things are made up of tiny building blocks known as cells.
You need to know all about eukaryotic cells — that's animal and plant cells to you and me...

Animal Cells

Animal cells contain the following things:

Nucleus

The nucleus has genes in it. Genes control what the cell does.

Cell membrane

This is a thin layer around the cell. It lets substances in and out.

Cytoplasm

This is where most of the chemical reactions in the cell happen.

Mitochondria

Where respiration happens.

Respiration is the way that cells turn food into energy.

Plant Cells

Plant cells contain the same things as animal cells. But, they have other things in them as well. Plant cells contain the following things:

Nucleus

The nucleus has genes in it. Genes control what the cell does.

Cell membrane

This is a thin layer around the cell. It lets substances in and out.

Cytoplasm

This is where most of the chemical reactions in the cell happen.

Cell wall

An outer layer which doesn't bend so the cell keeps its shape. This gives the cell structural support.

Vacuole

A large space filled with cell sap. It helps the cell keep its shape.

Mitochondria

Where respiration happens.

Photosynthesis is where plants use energy from sunlight to make food.

Chloroplasts

Where photosynthesis happens.

Cells, Tissues and Organs

All living things are made up of cells. Cells make up tissues and tissues make up organs.

Cells, Tissues, Organs and Organ Systems

1) A group of similar cells come together to make a tissue.
2) A group of different tissues work together to make an organ.
3) A group of organs work together to make an organ system.

Example: The Cardiovascular System

The cardiovascular system is the system that moves blood around the body.

1) Groups of cells make up different tissues.
2) Some of these tissues form the heart. The heart is an organ.
3) The heart and blood vessels make up an organ system called the cardiovascular system.

Cell

Tissue

Organ
(the heart)

heart

blood vessels

Organ system
(the cardiovascular system)

Practice Questions

1) What does the nucleus have in it?

2) Where do most of the chemical reactions in a cell happen?

3) Name one thing that is found in a plant cell but not in an animal cell.

4) True or false: a group of organs work together to make a tissue.

Section One — Biology

Cells, Tissues and Organs Questions

Q1   Use the words below to label the diagram of an **animal cell**.

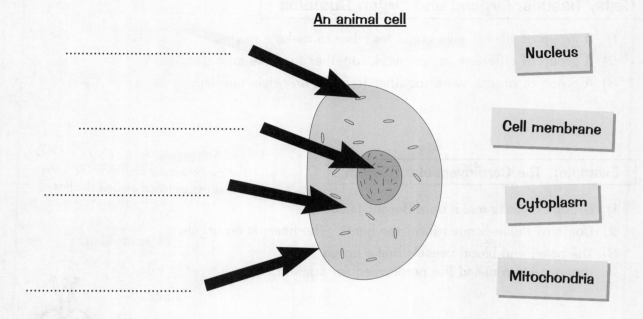

An animal cell

Nucleus

Cell membrane

Cytoplasm

Mitochondria

Q2   Draw a line to match the **part of the cell** with its **job**.
The first one has been done for you.

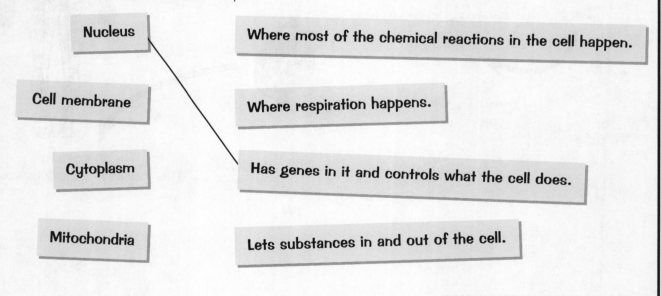

Nucleus

Cell membrane

Cytoplasm

Mitochondria

Where most of the chemical reactions in the cell happen.

Where respiration happens.

Has genes in it and controls what the cell does.

Lets substances in and out of the cell.

Q3 a)   Which part of a plant cell contains **cell sap**?

....

b)   Which part of the plant cell is where **photosynthesis** happens?

....

Cells, Tissues and Organs Questions

Q4   Use some of the words below to label the diagram of a **plant cell**.

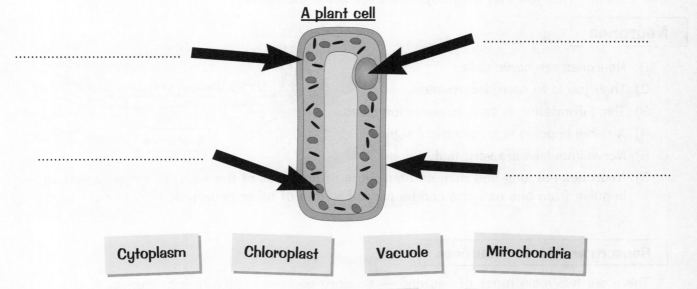

A plant cell

| Cytoplasm | Chloroplast | Vacuole | Mitochondria |

| Nucleus | Cell membrane | Cell wall |

Q5   Label the diagram using the following words:

| Organ | Tissue | Cell |

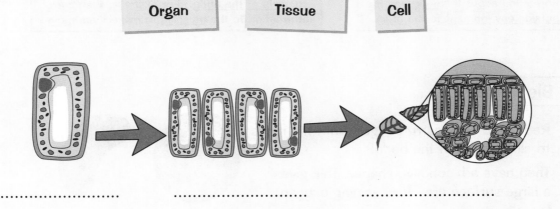

....

Q6   What is the **cardiovascular system**?   Circle the correct answer.

| An organ | A tissue | An organism | A cell | An organ system |

Animal Cells

Different cells do different jobs. This means that their structure (shape) needs to be right for their function (the job that they do). Here are some examples:

Neurones

1) Neurones are nerve cells.
2) Their job is to carry information.
3) This information is sent as nerve impulses.
4) A nerve impulse is an electrical signal.
5) Nerve impulses are very fast.
6) Neurones are long and thin, and have lots of branches at the end. This means that an impulse from one neurone can be passed to lots of other neurones.

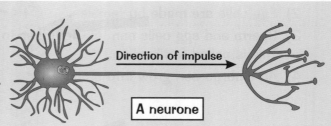

Direction of impulse

A neurone

Sensory and Motor Neurones

There are two main types of neurone — sensory neurones and motor neurones.

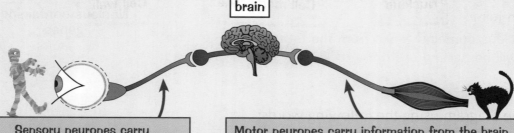

brain

Sensory neurones carry information about the body and the outside environment to the brain.

Motor neurones carry information from the brain to parts of the body. For example, they carry information to the muscles to make them move.

Red Blood Cells

1) Red blood cells carry oxygen from the lungs to all the cells in the body.
2) They have a biconcave shape. This gives a large surface area for carrying oxygen.
3) They don't have a nucleus. This makes more room to carry oxygen.

Biconcave means both sides curve inwards.

White Blood Cells

1) White blood cells defend the body against disease.
2) They are able to change shape. This lets white blood cells surround unwanted germs like bacteria and digest them.
3) They do have a nucleus.

white blood cells

Animal Cells

Sperm and Egg Cells

1) Sperm cells are made by males.
2) Egg cells are made by females.
3) Sperm and egg cells can join together to make an embryo. This is called fertilisation.
4) An embryo can grow into a child.

Sperm Cell

1) A sperm cell is very small.
2) It has a tail which can move.
3) This allows it to swim and find an egg to fertilise.
4) Its head contains enzymes. These are chemicals that help it get into an egg so the sperm and egg can join.
5) The nucleus contains genes from the father. These will be passed on to the child.

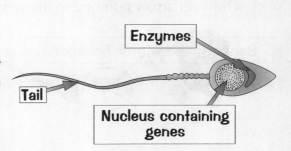

Egg Cell

1) An egg cell is large and bulky because it doesn't need to move about — it just sits and waits for sperm to find it.
2) It contains cytoplasm. This provides food for the embryo.
3) The nucleus contains genes from the mother. These will be passed on to the child.

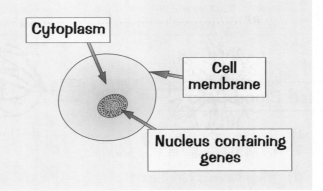

Practice Questions

1) What is a nerve impulse?

2) What shape are red blood cells?

3) What is the job of a white blood cell?

4) Why does a sperm cell have a tail?

5) What part of an egg cell provides food for an embryo?

Animal Cells Questions

Q1 a) What is a **neurone**? Circle the answer.

a muscle cell

a nerve cell

a nerve signal

someone who is very nervous

b) **Sensory neurones** are a type of neurone. Name one other type of neurone.

....

c) Draw an arrow pointing to the **sensory neurone** in the diagram below.

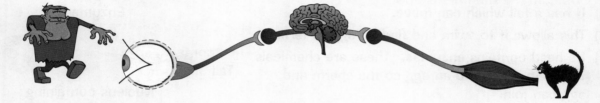

Q2 Label the animal cells using some of the words below.

a) ....

b) ....

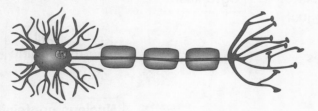

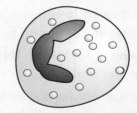

c) ....

d) ....

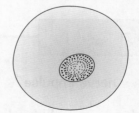

egg cell

red blood cell

sperm cell

white blood cell

neurone

Animal Cells Questions

Q3 Which of these statements are true, and which are false? Tick the correct boxes.

True False

a) The job of red blood cells is to defend the body against disease. ☐ ☐

b) Red blood cells have no nucleus. ☐ ☐

c) White blood cells have a biconcave shape. ☐ ☐

d) Red blood cells have a large surface area. ☐ ☐

Q4 The following statements are about egg and sperm cells.
Circle all the statements about **egg cells**.

They have a tail.

They contain genes from the father.

They contain cytoplasm.

They contain genes from the mother.

They are large and bulky.

They can swim.

Challenge Yourself

Q5 The picture shows a **sperm cell**.
Describe how the features shown help a sperm cell to **join** with an **egg cell**.

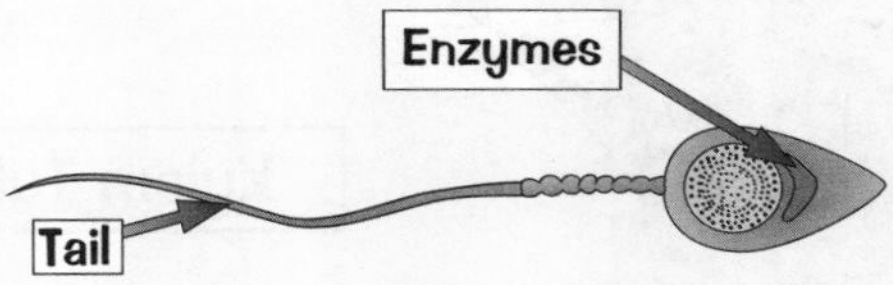

Enzymes

Tail

....

....

....

....

Plant Cells and Structures

Plants aren't just green mush on the inside. They're actually made up of lots of different cells...

Roots

A plant's roots are the bits of the plant below ground. They have two jobs:
1) They stop the plant blowing away or falling over. This is called anchorage.
2) They take in water from the soil.

Root Hair Cells

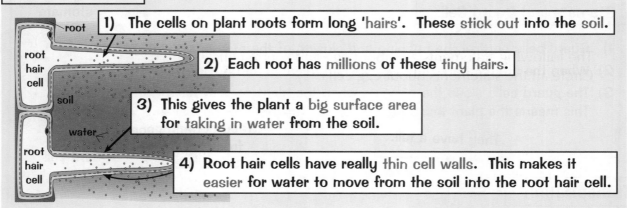

1) The cells on plant roots form long 'hairs'. These stick out into the soil.

2) Each root has millions of these tiny hairs.

3) This gives the plant a big surface area for taking in water from the soil.

4) Root hair cells have really thin cell walls. This makes it easier for water to move from the soil into the root hair cell.

Phloem and Xylem

Water and sugars are moved around plants in phloem and xylem tubes.
Phloem and xylem are found in the stem.

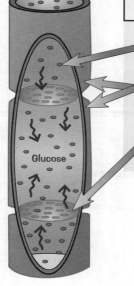

Phloem Tubes

1) Phloem tubes move glucose (a sugar) up and down the stem.

2) Phloem tubes are made up of cells joined together end to end.

3) The ends of each cell have little holes in them. This means glucose can move from one cell to the next.

Xylem Tubes

1) Xylem tubes carry water and minerals from the roots to the leaves.

2) They are made up of cells joined end to end.

3) The cells have no walls between them. This means that water and minerals can move from one cell to the next.

Minerals are things like iron and calcium which plants and animals need.

Plant Cells and Structures

Leaves

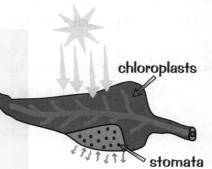

chloroplasts

stomata

1) The leaves are where photosynthesis takes place.
They make all the food that the plant needs.

2) Leaves contain lots of chloroplasts for photosynthesis.

3) During photosynthesis gases need to enter and exit the plant.
They do this through tiny holes called stomata.

Stomata and Guard Cells

stomata

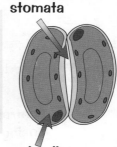

guard cell

1) Guard cells control the opening and closing of the stomata.

2) When the stomata are open, gases can move in and out of the leaf.

3) The guard cells close the stomata when the plant doesn't have water.
This means the plant loses less water vapour through the leaves.

Transpiration

Transpiration is when water is lost from a plant. Here's how it happens:

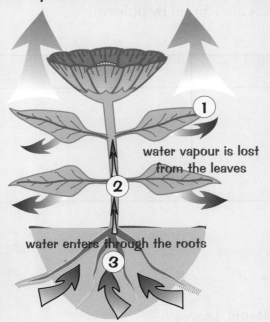

water vapour is lost from the leaves

water enters through the roots

1) Water vapour is lost from the leaves through the stomata.

2) There's less water in the leaves, so more water is drawn up the plant through the xylem tubes.

3) This draws water up from the roots.

Practice Questions

1) What do phloem tubes move up and down a stem?

2) Give one job done by a plant's roots.

Plant Cells and Structures Questions

Q1 The picture shows a **plant cell**.

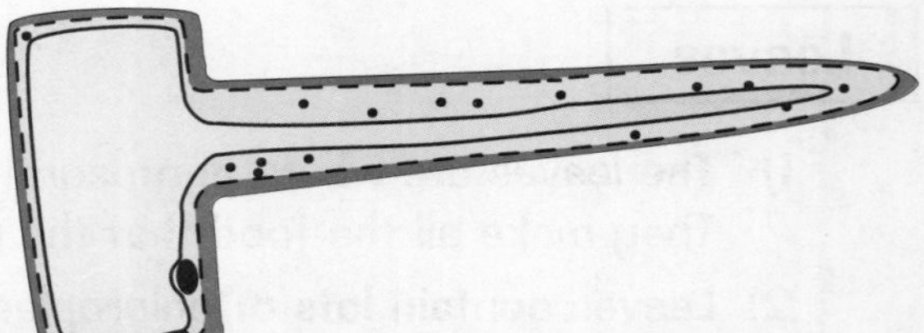

a) What type of plant cell is it?
Circle the correct answer.

guard cell   root hair cell   xylem cell

b) Where would you find this cell? Tick the correct box.

Roots ☐   Leaves ☐   Stem ☐

c) What **job** does it do? Circle the correct answer.

It controls the opening and closing of the stomata.

It takes up water from the soil.

It carries glucose up and down the stem.

Q2 Which **substances** are carried by **xylem** and which are carried by **phloem**?
Use the words below to fill in the table.

water

minerals

glucose

Xylem	Phloem

Q3 Are these statements about **roots** or **leaves**?
Tick the boxes.

		Roots	Leaves
a)	They provide anchorage for the plant.	☐	☐
b)	They are where photosynthesis takes place.	☐	☐
c)	They have stomata.	☐	☐
d)	They have cells which form long 'hairs'.	☐	☐

Plant Cells and Structures Questions

Q4   **Circle** the right words to complete the sentences.

> Guard cells are found in plant **roots** / **leaves**.
>
> They control the opening and closing of tiny holes called **root hair cells** / **stomata**.
>
> The holes close when the plant doesn't have much **oxygen** / **water**.
>
> This stops the plant from losing **water vapour** / **minerals**.

Q5   The diagram below shows a plant.

a)   Draw an **X** on the diagram where **water enters** the plant.

b)   Draw a **Y** on the diagram where **water exits** the plant.

c)   Draw an **arrow** on the stem to show the **direction** that water moves in.

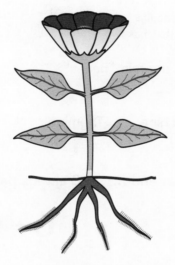

Challenge Yourself

Q6   Describe how **water** moves through a plant and is lost by **transpiration**.

....

....

....

....

Genes, Chromosomes and DNA

These pages are all about genetics. There are some tricky words coming up, so really focus.

Chromosomes

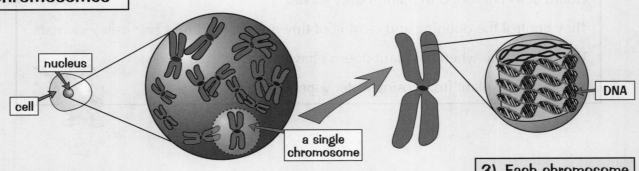

nucleus

cell

a single chromosome

DNA

1) **Cells** in your body have a **nucleus**.

2) **Chromosomes** are found in the **nucleus**.

3) Each **chromosome** is one very long bit of **DNA**.

DNA

1) **DNA** is a **double helix**.

2) Each of the two DNA strands contain "**bases**".

3) DNA has **four** different bases —

Adenine	Cytosine	Guanine	Thymine
A	**C**	**G**	**T**

4) **A** always pairs up with **T**   … and …   **C** always pairs up with **G**.

A double helix is a spiral that has two strands.

bases

strands

bases on one strand are joined to bases on the other strand

A + T   **C + G**

This is called complementary base-pairing.

| A | T | C | C | T | A | T | C | C | T | DNA strand |
| T | A | G | G | A | T | A | G | G | A | DNA strand |

Genes

1) A **gene** is a **short** bit of DNA.

2) Genes control your **characteristics**.

3) **Characteristics** are features. For example, dimples.

Genes, Chromosomes and DNA

Alleles

1) In the nucleus of each cell there are two copies of every chromosome.

 gene for eye colour

2) This means that each cell has two copies of every gene. For example, you've got two copies of the gene that controls your eye colour.

3) You can have different versions of the same gene. These are called alleles.

Allele for blue eyes.

Allele for brown eyes.

4) You might have two alleles the same. This is called homozygous.

You might have two different alleles. This is called heterozygous.

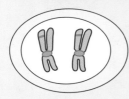 For example, two alleles for blue eyes.

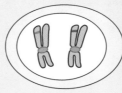 For example, an allele for blue eyes and an allele for brown eyes.

Controlling Characteristics

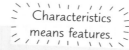 Characteristics means features.

1) Scientists use letters to show the alleles that an organism has.

2) You have two alleles for each gene. Each one can be either dominant or recessive.

3) Big letters like 'D' are used for dominant alleles.
   Small letters like 'd' are used for recessive ones.

 If both alleles are dominant, the dominant characteristic will be shown.

If both alleles are recessive, the recessive characteristic will be shown.

 If you have one dominant and one recessive allele only the dominant characteristic will be shown.

4) Genotype means what alleles you have. For example, Bb.

5) Phenotype means the actual characteristic you have. For example, brown eyes.

Practice Questions

1) Which base does cytosine (C) always pair up with?

2) What are different versions of the same gene called?

Section One — Biology

Genes, Chromosomes and DNA Questions

Q1   Use the words below to write the correct label on each diagram.

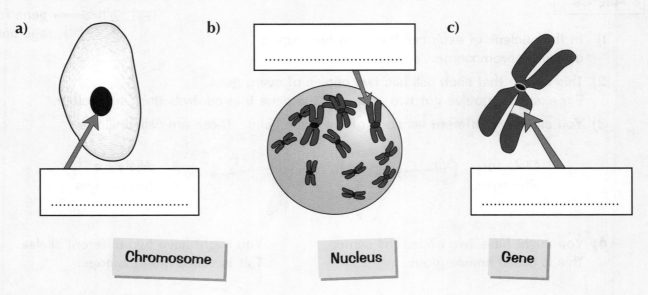

a)

....

b)

....

c)

....

Chromosome   Nucleus   Gene

Q2   Write letters in the boxes to show which **bases** pair up together in DNA.
One has been done for you.

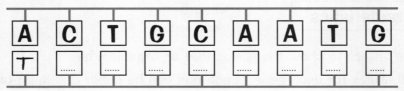

A	C	T	G	C	A	A	T	G
T	.....	.....	.....	.....	.....	.....	.....	.....

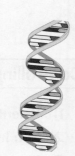

Q3   Draw a line to match the **word** with its **definition**.
One has been done for you.

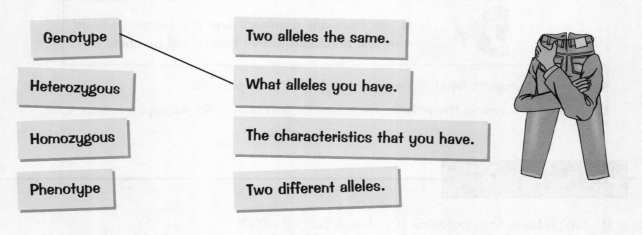

Genotype   Two alleles the same.

Heterozygous   What alleles you have.

Homozygous   The characteristics that you have.

Phenotype   Two different alleles.

Section One — Biology

Genes, Chromosomes and DNA Questions

Q4   Circle the right words in the sentences below.

a)   Chromosomes are found in the **cell wall** / **nucleus** of a cell.

b)   A gene is a short bit of **DNA** / **cytoplasm**.

c)   Your characteristics are controlled by your **genes** / **phenotype**.

Q5   You have two alleles for each gene.

a)   If both alleles are **dominant**, what characteristic will be shown? Circle the answer.

the recessive characteristic   the dominant characteristic

b)   If both alleles are **recessive**, what characteristic will be shown? Circle the answer.

the recessive characteristic   the dominant characteristic

c)   What characteristic will be shown if **one allele** is **recessive** and **one allele** is **dominant**? Circle the answer.

the recessive characteristic   the dominant characteristic

Challenge Yourself

Q6   Goldfish can either **read minds** or **control minds**.
Being able to **read minds** is caused by the **dominant** allele 'R'.
Being able to **control minds** is caused by the **recessive** allele 'r'.
Complete the table below using this information.

Genotype	Phenotype
RR	....
Rr	....
....	Control minds

Genetic Diagrams

Genetic diagrams can help you work out what characteristics (features) someone will end up with.

Punnett Squares

Genetic diagrams show how children get alleles from their parents. Here's an example:

1) The pigs at Bacon Farm can be pink. The normal pink colour is caused by the dominant allele 'N'.

2) The pigs can also be green. The green colour is caused by the recessive allele 'n'.

3) The genetic diagram below shows what could happen when two pink pigs have a piglet. Both pigs have one dominant allele and one recessive allele (Nn).

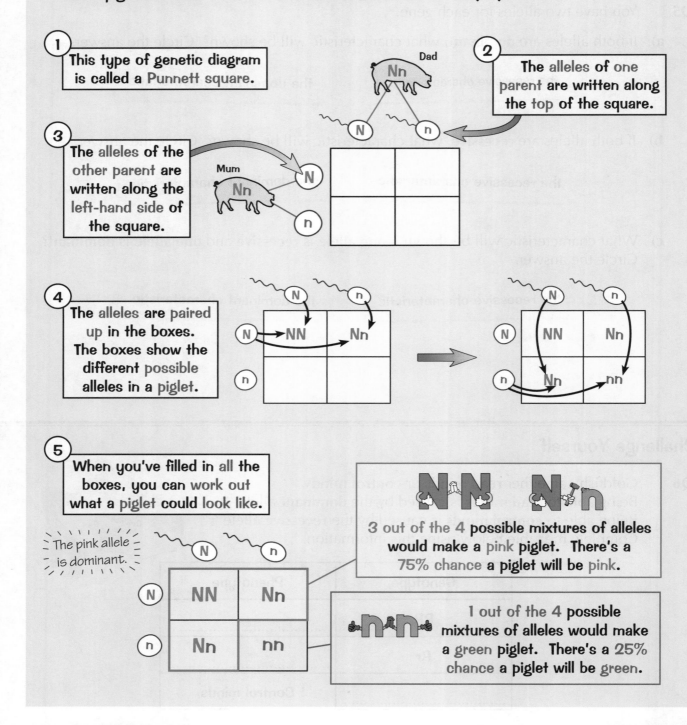

1 This type of genetic diagram is called a Punnett square.

Dad

2 The alleles of one parent are written along the top of the square.

3 The alleles of the other parent are written along the left-hand side of the square.

Mum

4 The alleles are paired up in the boxes. The boxes show the different possible alleles in a piglet.

	N	n
N	NN	Nn
n	Nn	nn

5 When you've filled in all the boxes, you can work out what a piglet could look like.

The pink allele is dominant.

	N	n
N	NN	Nn
n	Nn	nn

3 out of the 4 possible mixtures of alleles would make a pink piglet. There's a 75% chance a piglet will be pink.

1 out of the 4 possible mixtures of alleles would make a green piglet. There's a 25% chance a piglet will be green.

Genetic Diagrams

Family Trees

1) Family trees are another type of genetic diagram.

2) They show how alleles are passed on from parents to children.

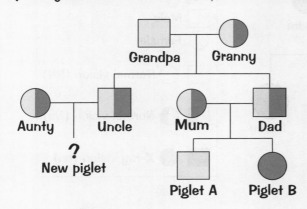

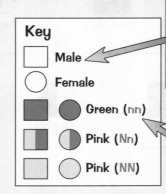

Key

☐ Male	
○ Female	
◼ ●	Green (nn)
◧ ◑	Pink (Nn)
▨ ◯	Pink (NN)

The shapes tell you whether the pig is a boy or a girl. In this family tree boys are squares and girls are circles.

The colour of the shapes tells you which alleles each pig has (nn, Nn or NN).

3) From the family tree you can see that Grandpa pig is pink because the colour of his square is pink. This means that he has the genotype NN.

4) Granny pig is also pink. The colour of her circle is pink and green so her genotype is Nn.

Pedigree Analysis

You can use a family tree to work out the probability of the children having a certain genotype. This is known as pedigree analysis. Here's an example:

1) Look at the family tree above. Aunty pig is pregnant.

2) Uncle pig and Aunty pig are both pink with the genotype Nn.

3) Using this information, you can draw a Punnett square.

4) From the Punnett square you can see that Aunty pig and Uncle pig have a:
   - 75% chance of having a pink piglet (NN / Nn).
   - 25% chance of having a green piglet (nn).

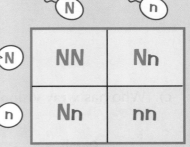

Practice Questions

1) True or false: a family tree is a type of genetic diagram.

2) Blue hair is dominant (H) and green hair is recessive (h). What hair colour would someone with the genotype Hh have?

Genetic Diagrams Questions

Q1 The **family tree** below shows a family with a gene for **x-ray vision**.

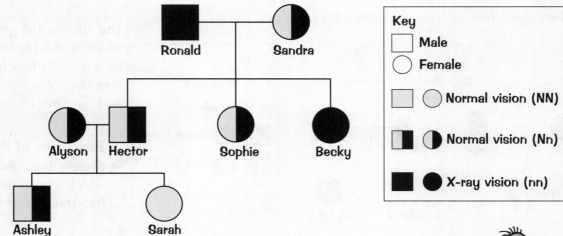

Key
- ☐ Male
- ◯ Female
- ◼ ⬤ Normal vision (NN)
- ◼ ◖ Normal vision (Nn)
- ◼ ⬤ X-ray vision (nn)

a) True or false: **Sophie**, **Becky** and **Alyson** are **sisters**.
Circle the correct answer.

True   **False**

b) What **alleles** does **Hector** have? Circle your answer.

NN   **Nn**   **nn**

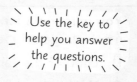

Use the key to help you answer the questions.

c) Who has **x-ray vision**? Circle the **two** correct answers.

Sarah   **Becky**   **Ashley**   **Ronald**

d) If **Alyson** and **Hector** had another **baby**, could it have **x-ray vision**?
Circle the correct answer.

Yes — the baby could have the alleles nn.

No — the baby could only have the alleles NN or Nn.

Genetic Diagrams Questions

Q2 In cats the allele for **black fur** (**B**) is **dominant**. The allele for **brown fur** (**b**) is **recessive**.

a) Two cats have kittens. Complete the diagram to show the **alleles** the kittens could get.

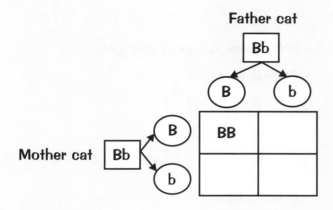

What colour fur will kittens with the following alleles have?

b) BB .... **c)** Bb .... **d)** bb ....

Q3 The allele for **dimples** (**D**) is **dominant**. The **allele** for no **dimples** (**d**) is **recessive**.

a) Jody and Mike are having a baby.
Complete the diagram to show the **alleles** they could pass on to the baby.

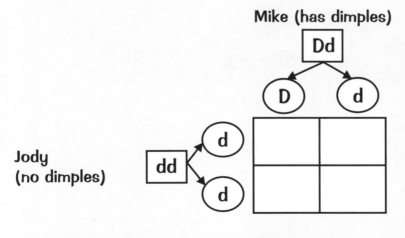

b) Will children with the following **alleles** have dimples? Write '**yes**' or '**no**'.

Dd .... dd ....

c) What is the **chance** of the baby having **dimples**? Circle the correct answer.

25%   50%   75%   100%

Genetic Mutations

A mutation is a change in a gene. This can be a good thing or a bad thing...

Mutations

1) Sometimes a gene mutates.

> A gene is a short piece of DNA (see page 16).

2) A mutation is where the order of the DNA bases in a gene changes.
   For example:

Original gene

T A T A G T C T T

changed base

T A T G G T C T T

Mutated gene

3) This can mean that the gene produces a new characteristic.

4) This new characteristic may be useful or harmful.

Useful Mutations

1) Sometimes a mutation can produce a useful characteristic in a plant or animal.

2) The useful characteristic may help the animal or plant to survive in its environment.

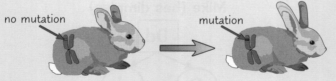

no mutation   mutation

Rabbit is born with <u>small ears</u>.   Rabbit is born with <u>big ears</u>.

Big ears gives the rabbit better hearing.
This may help the rabbit avoid other animals that want to eat it.

Harmful Mutations

1) Some mutations can be harmful.

2) For example, they can cause cancer. This is where a gene
   mutates and causes cells to grow out of control.

3) Mutations can also cause diseases known as genetic disorders.
   For example, cystic fibrosis (see next page).

Genetic Mutations

Genetic Disorder Example: Cystic Fibrosis

Mucus is a slimy mixture made by parts of the body.

1) Cystic fibrosis is an example of a genetic disorder.

2) Cystic fibrosis makes the body produce lots of mucus in the air passages, gut and pancreas.

3) This can then cause breathing problems and lung infections.

4) The allele that causes cystic fibrosis is recessive. It's written as a small f.

5) The mixture of alleles a person has decides whether they have cystic fibrosis or not:

ff	Ff	FF
Someone who has the disease.	A carrier of the disease (someone with only one copy of the recessive allele, so doesn't have the disease).	Normal.

6) Below is a family tree. It shows how cystic fibrosis can be passed on from parents to children:

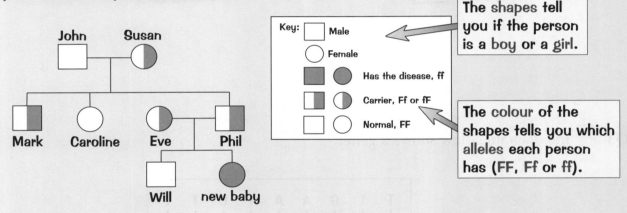

The shapes tell you if the person is a boy or a girl.

Key:
- Male
- Female
- Has the disease, ff
- Carrier, Ff or fF
- Normal, FF

The colour of the shapes tells you which alleles each person has (FF, Ff or ff).

7) Eve and Phil are both carriers (Ff). They carry the recessive allele, but they don't have the disease because they have a normal dominant allele (F).

8) The new baby has the disease (ff).
This is because she has got one f allele from Eve and one f allele from Phil.

Practice Questions

1) What happens to the DNA bases in a gene when it mutates?

2) True or false: mutations are always harmful.

Section One — Biology

Genetic Mutations Questions

Q1   Which of these statements are true and which are false? Tick the correct boxes.

                                          True False

a) Mutations are always useful.   ☐   ☐

b) A mutation is where the number of   ☐   ☐
      genes in a chromosome doubles.

Q2   What can mutations cause? Circle the correct answer.

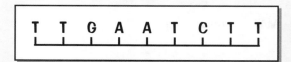

Q3   The diagram below shows a **gene**.

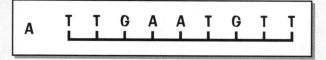

The gene **mutates**. Which of the following diagrams shows the mutated gene?
Circle your answer.

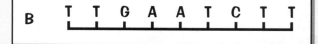

Genetic Mutations Questions

Q4 What is a **mutation**?
Circle the correct answer.

> The part of a cell where the DNA is found.

> A change in the order of the DNA bases in a gene.

> A new characteristic caused by a change in the environment.

Q5 The **family tree** below shows a family with a history of **cystic fibrosis**.

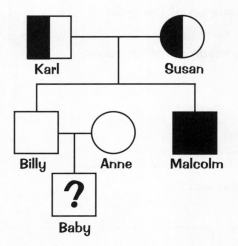

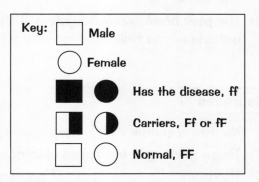

a) Which of these is true? Tick the box.

Susan has the disease. ☐

Susan is a carrier. ☐

b) What **alleles** does **Malcolm** have? ....

c) Could **Billy** and **Anne's** baby have **cystic fibrosis**?
Tick the correct box.

YES ☐   NO ☐

The Nervous System

The nervous system allows you to react to what goes on around you — it's pretty handy...

Receptors

1) Your eyes, ears, nose, tongue and skin all have different receptors in them.
2) Receptors are groups of cells that detect a stimulus.
3) A stimulus is a change in your environment.
4) For example, receptors in your ear detect sound and receptors in your skin detect heat.

The Nervous System

Your nervous system has two main bits:

1) The central nervous system (CNS) is made up of the brain and spinal cord.
2) The peripheral nervous system (PNS) is made up of neurones outside of the brain and spinal cord.

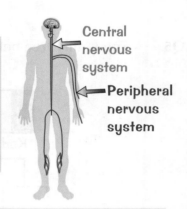
Central nervous system

Peripheral nervous system

Neurones

1) Neurones (nerve cells) carry messages to and from the CNS.
2) These messages are called electrical impulses.
3) There are two main types of neurones:

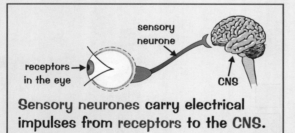

Sensory neurones carry electrical impulses from receptors to the CNS.

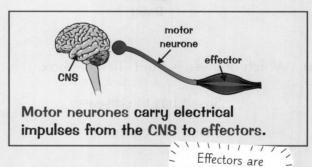

Motor neurones carry electrical impulses from the CNS to effectors.

Effectors are muscles or glands.

4) Here's how your brain responds (reacts) to a stimulus:

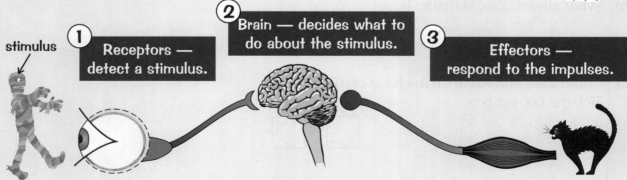

stimulus

① Receptors — detect a stimulus.

② Brain — decides what to do about the stimulus.

③ Effectors — respond to the impulses.

The Nervous System

Reflexes

1) Voluntary responses (reactions) are controlled by the brain.

2) They are things you decide to do. You have to think about them.

3) Reflexes are automatic responses. This means they just happen.

4) Reflexes are really fast because they're involuntary — you don't have to think about them.

5) They stop you from hurting yourself.

> You don't think about reflexes because they don't go through the brain.

Reflexes — Example

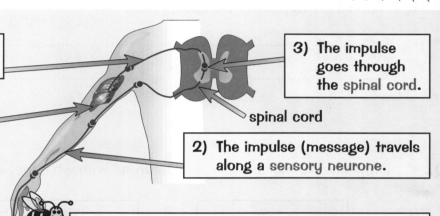

4) The impulse then travels along a motor neurone.

3) The impulse goes through the spinal cord.

spinal cord

5) The impulse reaches a muscle. The muscle contracts to move your hand away from the bee. This is the response.

2) The impulse (message) travels along a sensory neurone.

1) Receptors in the skin detect pain (a bee sting).

Synapses

1) Where neurones join together there's a tiny gap. This gap is called a synapse.

2) Here's what happens at a synapse:

① The electrical impulse reaches the end of a neurone.

③ The neurotransmitters set off a new electrical impulse in the next neurone.

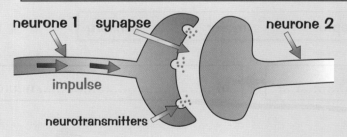

neurone 1   synapse   neurone 2

impulse

neurotransmitters

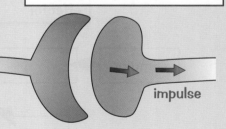

impulse

② This makes chemicals move across the synapse. The chemicals are called neurotransmitters.

Practice Questions

1) Name two types of neurones.

2) How is an impulse taken across the gap between neurones?

The Nervous System Questions

Q1 Some parts of the body make up the **CNS**.

a) What do the letters 'CNS' stand for? Tick the answer.

- [ ] central nervous system
- [ ] cardiac neurone system
- [ ] cellular nerve system

b) Name the **two** parts of the CNS.

1. ....

2. ....

Q2 Draw lines to match the type of **neurone** with what they do.

Sensory neurones...		... carry impulses from the CNS to effectors.

Motor neurones...		... carry impulses from receptors to the CNS.

Q3 The diagram below shows how the **CNS** decides what to do.
Label the diagram using the words in the box.

effector   receptor   motor   sensory

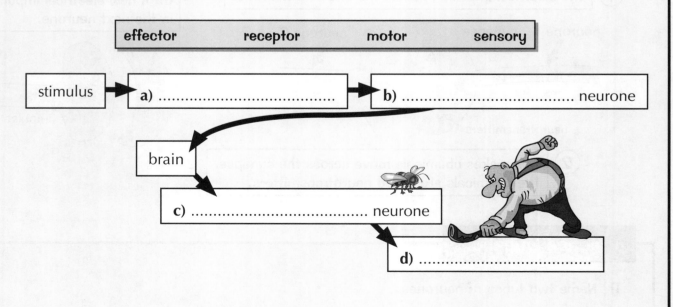

stimulus → a) .... → b) .... neurone

brain

c) .... neurone

d) ....

The Nervous System Questions

Q4 **Circle** the right words to complete the sentences.

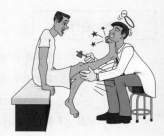

a) Reflexes are really **fast** / slow.

b) Reflexes stop you from hurting / **protecting** yourself.

c) Reflexes happen with / **without** you thinking about them.

d) A synapse is a tiny gap where two receptors / **neurones** join together.

e) **Neurotransmitters** / Electrical impulses take messages across synapses.

Q5 The diagram shows the path of a **reflex**.

a) Draw lines to match the letters from the diagram to their names. One has been done for you.

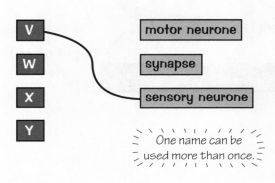

One name can be used more than once.

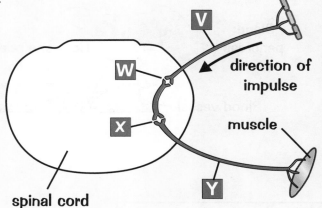

receptor in skin

direction of impulse

muscle

spinal cord

b) Circle the right word to complete the sentence below.

In this reflex the muscle acts as the **effector** / receptor.

Challenge Yourself

Q6 Describe what happens at a **synapse**.

....

....

....

....

Hormones

Nerves aren't the only way information is sent around the body. The body also uses hormones.

Hormones

1) Hormones are chemicals.
2) They're released by glands in the body.
3) Glands that make hormones are called endocrine glands.
4) All of the endocrine glands in your body make up the endocrine system.

How Hormones Work

1) Hormones are carried around the body in the blood.
2) Some organs respond (do something) when the hormone reaches them.
3) Organs that respond are called target organs.
4) For example:

Organs are things like the liver, heart and lungs.

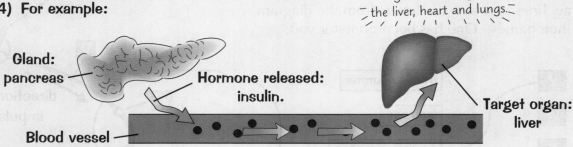

Gland: pancreas

Hormone released: insulin.

Target organ: liver

Blood vessel

Nerves vs Hormones

Nerves and hormones both carry information around the body.
But there are some differences:

Nerves...	carry information quickly...	and the response lasts for a short time...	because they carry information as electrical impulses.
Hormones...	carry information slowly...	and the response lasts a long time...	because they carry information in the blood.

HMS Hormone

Hormones

Controlling Blood Sugar Level

1) Blood sugar level is the amount of glucose (a sugar) in the blood.
2) It's kept steady by hormones called insulin and glucagon.
3) Insulin and glucagon are made by a gland called the pancreas.
4) Here's how it all works...

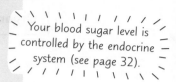

Your blood sugar level is controlled by the endocrine system (see page 32).

Insulin

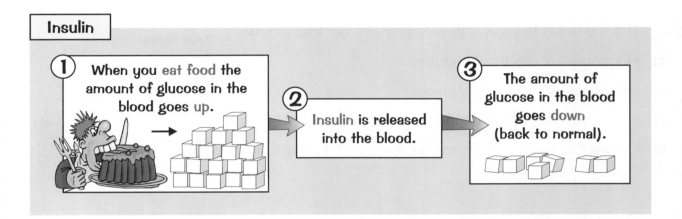

① When you eat food the amount of glucose in the blood goes up.

② Insulin is released into the blood.

③ The amount of glucose in the blood goes down (back to normal).

Glucagon

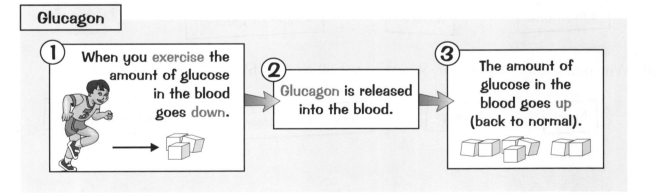

① When you exercise the amount of glucose in the blood goes down.

② Glucagon is released into the blood.

③ The amount of glucose in the blood goes up (back to normal).

Practice Questions

1) What are the glands that release hormones called?

2) How are hormones carried around the body?

3) True or false: hormones carry information faster than nerves.

4) Name a hormone that controls blood glucose level.

Hormones Questions

Q1   What is the **endocrine system** made up of?   Circle the answer.

Organs that make blood.

Glands that make hormones.

Nerves that release hormones.

Q2   Tick the boxes to show if these statements are **true** or **false**.

		True	False
a)	Hormones are electrical impulses.	☐	☐
b)	Hormones are released by glands.	☐	☐
c)	Hormones are carried around the body in the blood.	☐	☐
d)	Organs that respond to hormones are called response organs.	☐	☐

Q3   The body controls your **blood sugar** level.

a)   What is **insulin**?   Circle one.

a hormone   a nerve   a type of glucose

b)   Which of the following is involved in controlling your blood sugar level?   Circle one.

heart   lungs   endocrine system   nervous system

Q4   Tick the boxes to answer these questions about nerves and hormones.

		Nerves	Hormones
a)	Which carries information faster?		
b)	Which causes the response which lasts the longest?		
c)	Which carries information in the blood?		

Hormones Questions

Q5 Which **hormones raise** and **lower blood glucose level**?
Match the hormone to the action.

glucagon   insulin

a)
> **Action**: raises blood glucose level
>
> **Hormone**: ....

b)
> **Action**: lowers blood glucose level
>
> **Hormone**: ....

Q6 Complete this flow chart by circling one word from each pair.

a) Eating makes the amount of glucose in the blood go **up / down**.

b) Glucose / insulin is released into the blood.

c) The blood glucose level goes **up / down**.

Challenge Yourself

Q7 Exercising lowers the level of glucose in the blood.
Describe how the body returns the glucose level to normal.

....

....

....

Section One — Biology

Homeostasis

Homeostasis sounds pretty scary, but it's not too bad... scout's promise.

Homeostasis

1) Homeostasis means keeping conditions inside your body the same.
2) This means that your cells can work properly.
3) Homeostasis uses information sent by hormones and nerves.

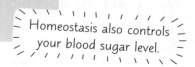

Homeostasis also controls your blood sugar level.

Body Temperature Regulation

Sometimes you get too hot or too cold.

1) When this happens your body does things to bring the temperature back to normal.
2) This is called body temperature regulation.
3) Body temperature regulation is a type of homeostasis.
4) It is controlled by your nervous system.

When You're Too Hot:

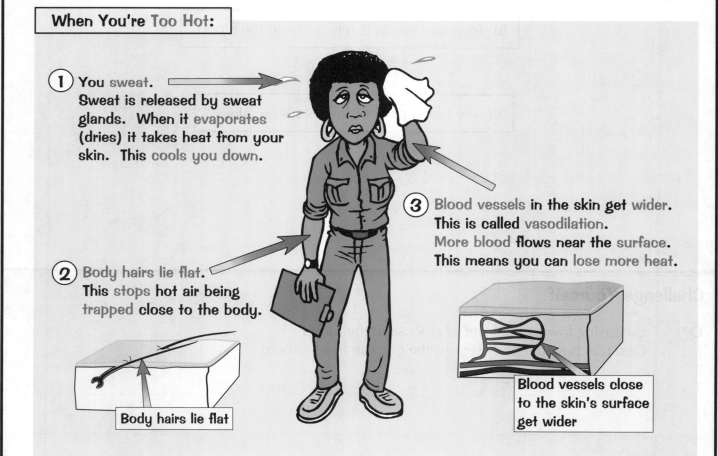

1 You sweat.
Sweat is released by sweat glands. When it evaporates (dries) it takes heat from your skin. This cools you down.

2 Body hairs lie flat.
This stops hot air being trapped close to the body.

Body hairs lie flat

3 Blood vessels in the skin get wider. This is called vasodilation. More blood flows near the surface. This means you can lose more heat.

Blood vessels close to the skin's surface get wider

Homeostasis

When You're Too Cold:

① You **shiver**.
This **movement** helps to
keep you warm.

② **Body hairs stand on end**.
This **traps air** to keep you warm.

③ **Blood vessels** in the skin
get **narrower**. This is called
vasoconstriction. Less blood
flows near the surface.
This means less heat is lost.

Body hairs stand on end

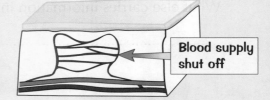

Blood supply shut off

It is very cold so the hair on the backs
of these dogs is standing on end.

Practice Questions

1) True or false: homeostasis helps your cells to work properly.

2) What happens to your body temperature when you sweat?

3) When you're too hot, do your blood vessels get narrower or get wider?

4) Give two things your body does when you're too cold.

Homeostasis Questions

Q1 a) What does **homeostasis** mean? Circle the answer.

A — Keeping conditions outside your body the same.

B — Keeping conditions inside your body the same.

b) Which of these is an example of homeostasis? Circle the answer.

Body temperature regulation

Gene mutations

The nervous system

c) Homeostasis uses information sent by **nerves**.
What else carries information in homeostasis?

....

Q2 Fill in the table to show whether the actions **warm up** or **cool down** the body.
One's been done for you.

shivering   ~~sweating~~   body hair standing
on end   more blood flowing
near the surface

Warm Up	Cool Down
	sweating

Homeostasis Questions

Q3 The diagrams below show things that happen as part of **body temperature regulation**.
Label each diagram using the words below.

When you're too hot   **When you're too cold**

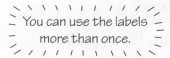
You can use the labels more than once.

a)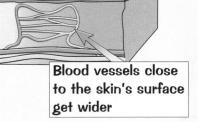

Blood vessels close to the skin's surface get wider

....

b)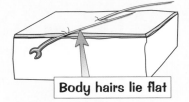

Body hairs lie flat

....

c)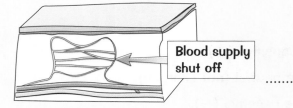

Blood supply shut off

....

Challenge Yourself

Q4 When Bob goes for a run his body temperature starts to rise.
Explain how **vasodilation** helps to cool him down.

....

....

....

Section One — Biology

Atoms and Elements

Everything is made up of atoms. They're really, really tiny.

Atoms

Atoms have a nucleus and electrons. Here is a drawing of an atom.

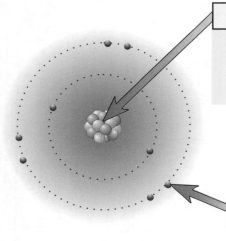

The Nucleus

1) The nucleus is really small compared to the whole atom.

2) It's made up of protons ⬤ and neutrons ⚪ .

The Electrons

Electrons surround the nucleus in shells (energy levels).

Charge and Mass in Atoms

The parts of an atom have different charges.

1) Protons are positive (+).

2) Neutrons are neutral (not charged).

3) Electrons are negative (−).

The relative masses of parts of an atom are:

	Mass
Proton	1
Neutron	1
Electron	Very tiny

1) Protons and neutrons have the same mass.

2) The mass of electrons is much smaller.

Atoms and Elements

Atoms and the Number of Electrons

In an atom there will always be the same number of protons and electrons.

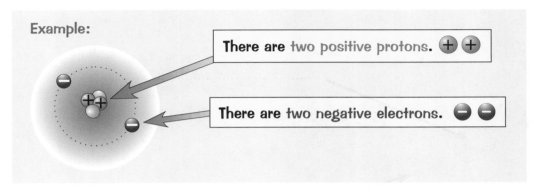

Example:

There are two positive protons. ➕ ➕

There are two negative electrons. ➖ ➖

Protons and the Type of Atom

The number of protons ⚪ decides what type of atom it is.

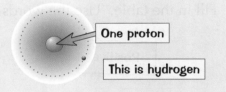

1) For example, all hydrogen atoms have one proton. All helium atoms have two protons.

One proton

This is hydrogen

2) If a substance only has one type of atom it's called an element.

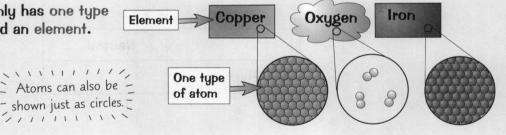

Element ➡ Copper   Oxygen   Iron

Atoms can also be shown just as circles.

One type of atom

Practice Questions

1) What is the nucleus made up of?

2) Are protons positive or negative?

3) An atom has 4 electrons. How many protons will it have?

4) What is an element?

Atoms and Elements Questions

Q1   Use the words in the box to label the picture.

Electron   Nucleus

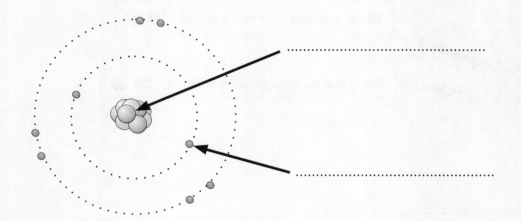

Q2   Fill in the table. Use the words below.

Positive   Neutron   Negative

Part of the atom	Charge
Proton	
	Neutral
Electron	

Q3   Read the two sentences below. Tick the one that is **true**.

The nucleus is made up of protons and electrons.   ☐

The nucleus is made up of protons and neutrons.   ☐

Atoms and Elements Questions

Q4   Look at these diagrams of substances. Circle the two that are **elements**.

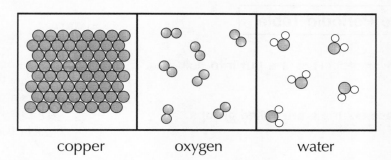

copper   oxygen   water

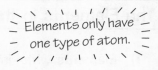

Elements only have
one type of atom.

Q5   The diagrams below aren't finished.

Write down how many **electrons** each atom should have.

a)

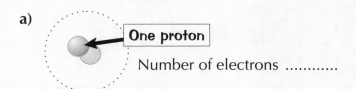

One proton

Number of electrons ....

b)

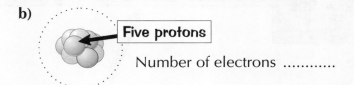

Five protons

Number of electrons ....

c)

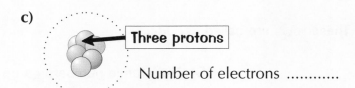

Three protons

Number of electrons ....

d)

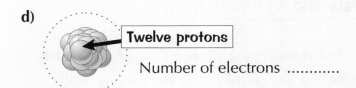

Twelve protons

Number of electrons ....

The Periodic Table

Scientists use a table to organise the elements.

The Elements in the Periodic Table

1) Elements with similar properties are put into columns.

2) These columns are called groups.

Properties are things like whether it's a gas, liquid or solid OR whether it conducts heat.

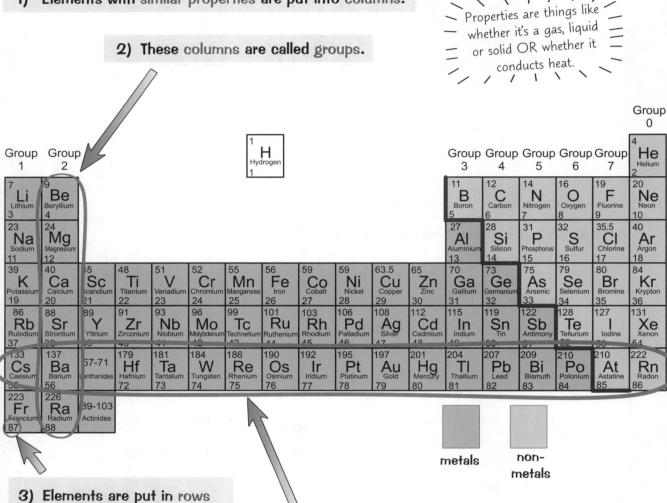

metals

non-metals

3) Elements are put in rows in order of atomic number.

4) These rows are called periods.

5) The atomic numbers go up across each period.

Metals and Non-metals

1) The elements are either metals or non-metals.

2) Metals are on the left of the periodic table.

3) Non-metals are on the right of the periodic table.

The Periodic Table

Group Number

Each group in the periodic table has a number. For example, Group 1 or Group 6.

1) All of the elements in a group have the same number of electrons in their outer shell.

2) This is why elements in the same group have similar properties.

3) The number of electrons in the outer shell is the same as the group number.

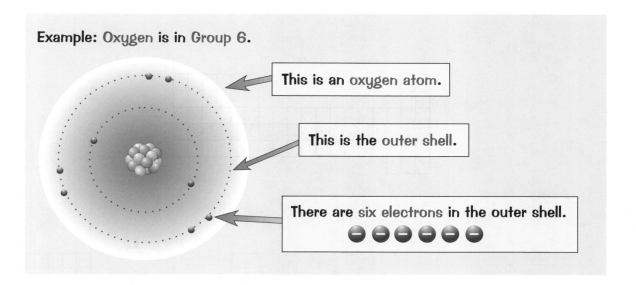

Example: Oxygen is in Group 6.

This is an oxygen atom.

This is the outer shell.

There are six electrons in the outer shell.

Mass Number and Atomic Number

Each element in the periodic table has a mass number and an atomic number.

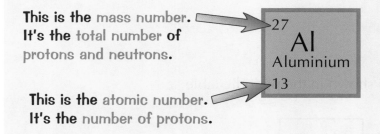

This is the mass number. It's the total number of protons and neutrons.

27
Al
Aluminium
13

This is the atomic number. It's the number of protons.

The number of neutrons is the mass number take away the atomic number.
E.g. for aluminium, 27 − 13 = 14.

Remember, number of protons is the same as number of electrons.

Practice Questions

1) What are the columns in the periodic table called?

2) What are the rows in the periodic table called?

3) True or false: all of the elements in a group have different numbers of electrons in their outer shells.

The Periodic Table Questions

Q1   One of the diagrams below shows a **group** in the periodic table. Circle the one that does.

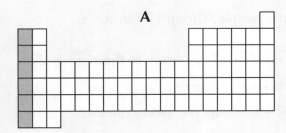

A

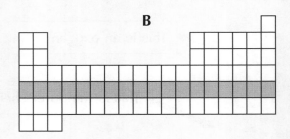

B

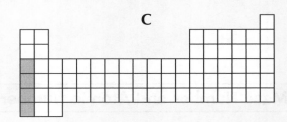

C

Q2   The diagram shows how **sodium** is shown in the periodic table.

$$^{23}_{11}\text{Na}$$

a) Circle the **atomic number** on the diagram.

b) How many **protons** does sodium have? ....

The Periodic Table Questions

Q3 What is the **mass number** of an element? Tick the box.

☐ The total number of neutrons and electrons.

☐ The total number of protons and neutrons.

☐ The total number of protons and electrons.

Q4 Elements in the **same group** have **similar properties**.

a) Tick the pair of elements that has similar properties.

Look at the periodic table on the inside front cover of this book to help you.

☐ potassium and rubidium

☐ helium and fluorine

b) Sodium and potassium react with water in a similar way.
Circle the right words in the sentences below.

One has been done for you.

Sodium and potassium are both in (Group 1) / Group 2.

This means they have the same number of neutrons / **electrons** in their outer shell.

This gives them **similar** / different properties.

Challenge Yourself

Q5 Explain how you would use the periodic table to find the **number of electrons** in the **outer shell** of a carbon atom.

....

....

....

Chemical Substances and Formulas

There are different types of chemical substances...

Types of Chemical Substances

All substances are made up of atoms.

Elements

1) A substance with only one type of atom is called an element.

2) For example, carbon and oxygen are elements.

Carbon   Oxygen

Reminder
You've met elements before, on page 41.

Compounds

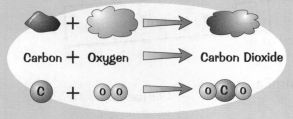

Carbon + Oxygen ⟶ Carbon Dioxide

1) Compounds are made when atoms of two or more elements are chemically combined (joined) together.

2) For example, carbon dioxide is a compound. It's made from a chemical reaction between carbon and oxygen.

Mixtures

1) Mixtures are substances that are not chemically joined up.

2) For example, air is a mixture of gases:

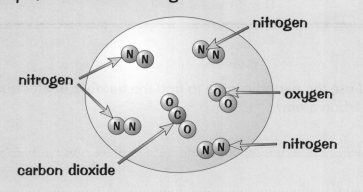

nitrogen

nitrogen

oxygen

nitrogen

carbon dioxide

Chemical Substances and Formulas

Symbols

Scientists use letters for the names of elements.

> 1) Each element has a one or two letter symbol.
> 2) For example:
>
> | | | |
> |---|---|---|
> | C = carbon | O = oxygen | Na = sodium |
> | Cu = copper | Mg = magnesium | Ca = calcium |
>
> 3) You can find the symbol for any element in the periodic table.

Molecules

> 1) Atoms joined together make molecules.
> 2) For example, ⓞⓞ = an oxygen molecule.
> 3) If the atoms in a molecule are the same it's called an element.
>   So oxygen ⓞⓞ is an element.
> 4) If the atoms in a molecule are different it's called a compound.
>   So carbon dioxide ⓞⒸⓞ is a compound.

Formulas

Formulas are a quick way to write chemicals — they save you from writing out the whole name.

> 1) Molecular formulas show you what kind of atoms there are and how many there are.
> 2) For example, the molecular formula of carbon dioxide ⓞⒸⓞ is CO_2.

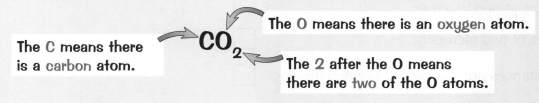

The C means there is a carbon atom.

The O means there is an oxygen atom.

The 2 after the O means there are two of the O atoms.

Practice Questions

> 1) True or false: mixtures are substances that are not chemically joined up.
>
> 2) What is a compound?

Chemical Substances and Formulas Questions

Q1   Some chemicals are shown below. Which ones are **molecules**?
Circle **three** answers.

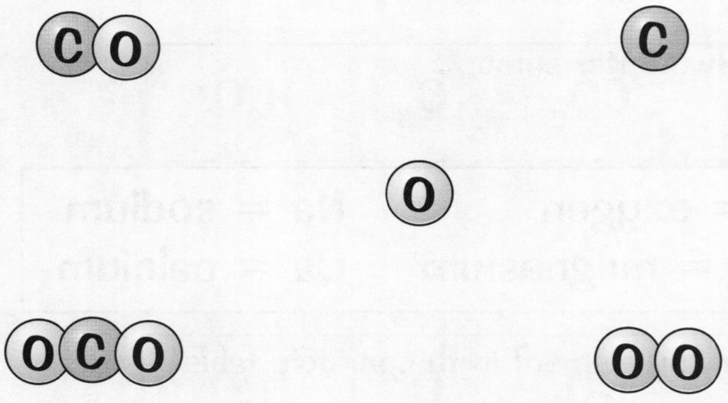

CO C

O

OCO OO

Q2   Some chemicals are shown below. Which ones are **compounds**?
Circle **two** answers.

Don't get elements and compounds mixed up.

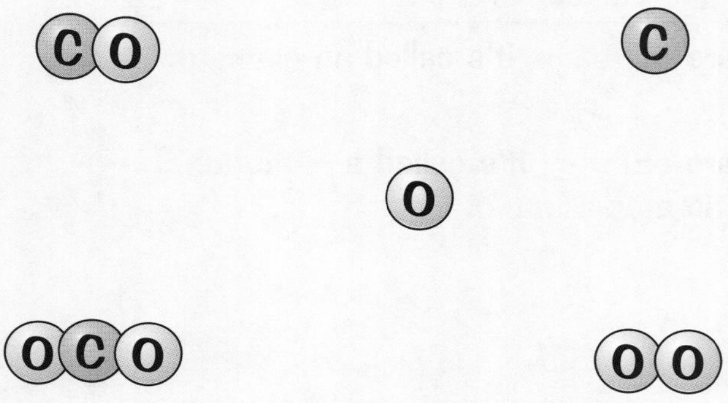

CO C

O

OCO OO

Q3 a)   Which of these is a **molecule**? Tick the right answer.

Two atoms joined together.   ☐

A mixture of two elements.   ☐

Two substances not chemically bonded together. ☐

b)   Which of these is a **compound**? Tick the right answer.

A molecule made of two atoms the same.   ☐

A molecule made of two different atoms.   ☐

Two substances not chemically bonded together. ☐

Chemical Substances and Formulas Questions

Q4   Answer the questions below by circling the right **formula**.

a) Which chemical has **two oxygen** atoms in it?

$$CH_4 \qquad CO_2 \qquad O_3 \qquad H_2O$$

b) Which chemical has **two hydrogen** atoms in it?

$$CH_4 \qquad CO_2 \qquad O_3 \qquad H_2O$$

c) Which chemical has **hydrogen** and **oxygen** atoms in it?

$$CH_4 \qquad CO_2 \qquad O_3 \qquad H_2O$$

Q5   Write the **symbols** for the elements below.

a) Oxygen   ....

b) Magnesium   ....

c) Copper   ....

Use the periodic table on the inside front cover of this book to help you.

Q6   Look at the **formula**.

$$NH_4$$

Are these sentences **true** or **false**? Tick the boxes.

True False

a) The substance is an element.   ☐   ☐

b) The substance contains five atoms.   ☐   ☐

c) There is carbon in the substance.   ☐   ☐

d) The substance contains nitrogen and hydrogen. ☐   ☐

Electron Shells

Electrons move round the nucleus in <u>shells</u>.

Electron Shell Rules

You need to learn how many electrons go in each shell.

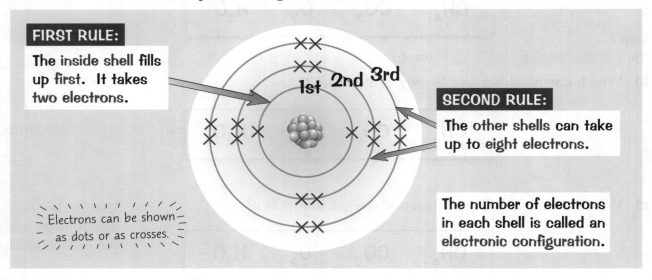

FIRST RULE:
The inside shell fills up first. It takes two electrons.

1st 2nd 3rd

SECOND RULE:
The other shells can take up to eight electrons.

The number of electrons in each shell is called an electronic configuration.

Electrons can be shown as dots or as crosses.

The First 20 Elements

Here are the electronic configurations of the first 20 elements.

H Hydrogen							He Helium
1 Proton no. = 1							2 Proton no. = 2
Li Lithium	Be Beryllium	B Boron	C Carbon	N Nitrogen	O Oxygen	F Fluorine	Ne Neon
2,1 Proton no. = 3	2,2 Proton no. = 4	2,3 Proton no. = 5	2,4 Proton no. = 6	2,5 Proton no. = 7	2,6 Proton no. = 8	2,7 Proton no. = 9	2,8 Proton no. = 10
Na Sodium	Mg Magnesium	Al Aluminium	Si Silicon	P Phosphorus	S Sulfur	Cl Chlorine	Ar Argon
2,8,1 Proton no. = 11	2,8,2 Proton no. = 12	2,8,3 Proton no. = 13	2,8,4 Proton no. = 14	2,8,5 Proton no. = 15	2,8,6 Proton no. = 16	2,8,7 Proton no. = 17	2,8,8 Proton no. = 18
K Potassium	Ca Calcium						
2,8,8,1 Proton no. = 19	2,8,8,2 Proton no. = 20						

Reminder
The number of protons is the same as the number of electrons.

Electron Shells

Using the Rules

Example: Nitrogen has seven protons. That means it's also got 7 electrons.
Follow the 'Electron Shell Rules' to work out its electronic configuration.

Step 1:
The inside shell can only take 2 electrons.

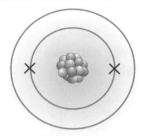

Two of the seven electrons go into the first shell.

Step 2:
The second shell can take up to 8 electrons.

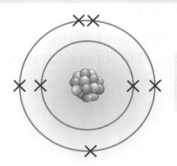

The five left over electrons go into the second shell.

You can write out the electronic configuration of nitrogen like this:

Two of the seven electrons go into the first shell.

The five left over electrons go into the second shell.

Don't forget this.

You can use the 'Electron Shell Rules' to work out the electronic configuration of any element.

Practice Questions

1) Which shell fills up with electrons first?

2) How many electrons can the second shell hold?

3) Use the 'Electron Shell Rules' to write out the electronic configuration of argon.
Argon has 18 protons.

4) Give the electronic configuration of sodium. Sodium has 11 electrons.

Electron Shells Questions

Q1 Are these sentences **true** or **false**? Tick the boxes.

True **False**

a) In atoms, electrons can be found in shells. ☐ ☐

b) The first shell can only have 2 electrons. ☐ ☐

Q2 Fluorine has **9 protons**.

a) How many electrons does fluorine have? ....

b) Draw these electrons onto the **shells** in the diagram below.
Draw a cross (X) to show each electron.

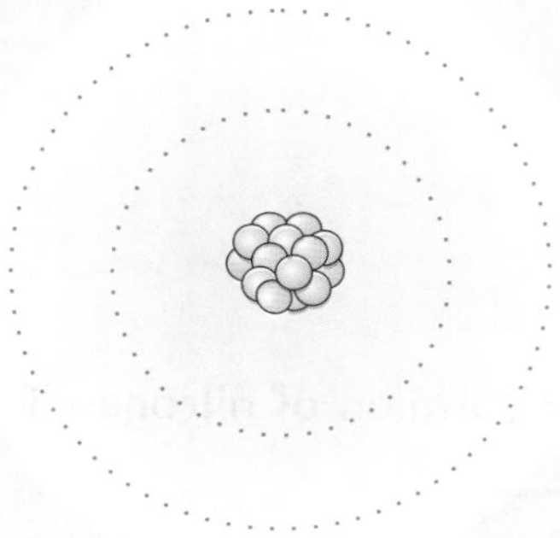

c) How many more electrons could the outer shell take? Circle your answer.

1   0   7

Q3 Write out the **electronic configuration** for the elements below.
The number of electrons in each element is given in brackets.

Beryllium (4 electrons) .... 2, 2 .... *One has been done for you.*

a) Oxygen (8 electrons) ....

b) Magnesium (12 electrons) ....

c) Silicon (14 electrons) ....

Electron Shells Questions

Q4   **Chlorine** has 17 protons.

a)   What is its electronic configuration?

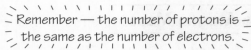

Remember — the number of protons is the same as the number of electrons.

.... , ... , ...

b)   Draw the electrons on the shells in the diagram. Use a cross (X) for each electron.

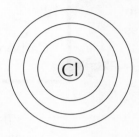

c)   How many shells are **full** in a chlorine atom?

....

Q5   Draw the **electronic configurations** for these elements.
(The first one has been done for you.)

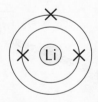

Lithium (3 electrons)

a) Nitrogen (7 electrons)

b) Magnesium (12 electrons)

Relative Atomic Mass and Isotopes

This sounds a bit tricky, but don't worry. Just take it step by step.

Relative Atomic Mass

In the periodic table, the elements all have two numbers.

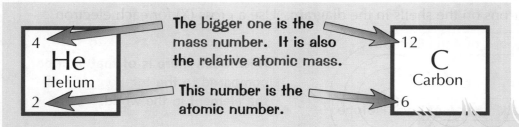

The bigger one is the mass number. It is also the relative atomic mass.

This number is the atomic number.

Reminder
The mass number is the total number of protons and neutrons.

Isotopes

1) Atoms of the same element always have the same number of protons.

2) But atoms of the same element can have different numbers of neutrons.

3) Isotopes are atoms of the same element, which have the same number of protons but a different number of neutrons.

---

1) For example, all carbon atoms have six protons.

2) One form of carbon has a mass number of 12. It is called carbon-12.

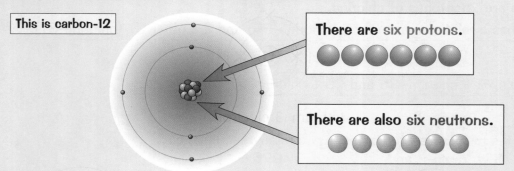

This is carbon-12

There are six protons.

There are also six neutrons.

3) Another form of carbon has a mass number of 14. It is called carbon-14.

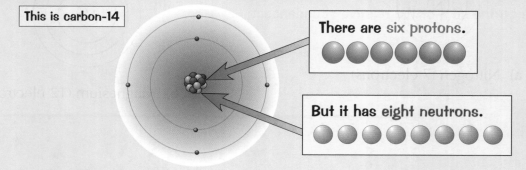

This is carbon-14

There are six protons.

But it has eight neutrons.

4) Carbon-12 and carbon-14 are two isotopes of carbon.

Relative Atomic Mass and Isotopes

Working out Relative Atomic Mass

You can work out the relative atomic mass of an element.

You need to know two things:

1 The relative mass of each isotope

2 The relative abundance of each isotope

How much there is of that isotope compared to the <u>total amount</u> of the element in the world.

Then:

1) **Times** the **mass** of each isotope by its **relative abundance.**

2) **Add** together the answers you get.

3) **Divide** by the **sum** of the relative abundances.

Sum just means add them all together.

The answer might not be a whole number. It might be a decimal.

Example

Work out the relative atomic mass of chlorine.

1 There are 2 isotopes of chlorine.
One has a relative mass of 35 (chlorine-35) and the other 37 (chlorine-37).

2 There's 75% chlorine-35 and 25% chlorine-37 in the world.

1) Times the mass of each isotope by its relative abundance:
$35 \times 75 = 2625$ and $37 \times 25 = 925$

2) Add together the answers you get: $2625 + 925 = 3550$

3) Divide by the sum of the relative abundances: $\dfrac{3550}{75 + 25} = 35.5$

Practice Questions

1) What are isotopes?

2) What is the relative abundance of an isotope?

Relative Atomic Mass and Isotopes Questions

Q1   **Complete** this sentence.

> Isotopes of the same element have the same number of
>
> protons but a different number of ....

Q2   Look at the information about some atoms below.

X
$^{12}_{6}C$

Y
$^{14}_{7}N$

Z
$^{14}_{6}C$

number of protons   ....6........   ....7........   ....6........

number of neutrons   ....6........   ....7........   ....8........

Which two of the atoms are **isotopes** of each other? Circle the answer.

| X and Y | X and Z | Y and Z |

Q3   Are these sentences **true** or **false**? Tick the boxes.

True False

a)   The relative atomic mass of an element is always a whole number.   ☐ ☐

b)   Isotopes of the same element have different numbers of electrons.   ☐ ☐

Relative Atomic Mass and Isotopes Questions

Q4 A sample of oxygen contains the **isotopes** oxygen-16 and oxygen-18.

a) What is the **mass number** of oxygen-16? Tick the answer.

☐ 8   ☐ 16

☐ 10   ☐ 18

b) The sample is 99.8% oxygen-16 and 0.2% oxygen-18.

Write down the **relative abundance** of oxygen-16. ....

c) Calculate the **relative atomic mass** of oxygen.

$$\text{Relative atomic mass of oxygen} = \frac{\left(\begin{array}{c}\text{Mass number} \\ \text{of oxygen-16}\end{array} \times \begin{array}{c}\text{Relative abundance} \\ \text{of oxygen-16}\end{array}\right) + \left(\begin{array}{c}\text{Mass number} \\ \text{of oxygen-18}\end{array} \times \begin{array}{c}\text{Relative abundance} \\ \text{of oxygen-18}\end{array}\right)}{\text{Sum of relative abundances}}$$

$$= \frac{(\ldots\ldots\ldots \times \ldots\ldots\ldots) + (\ldots\ldots\ldots \times \ldots\ldots\ldots)}{\ldots\ldots\ldots + \ldots\ldots\ldots}$$

$$= \ldots\ldots\ldots$$

Challenge Yourself

Q5 A sample of copper (Cu) contains 70% Cu-63 and 30% Cu-65.
Calculate the **relative atomic mass** of copper.

....

....

....

....

....

Equations

You need to know about chemical equations.

Chemical Equations

Chemical equations show what happens in a reaction.

> 1) In a chemical reaction **chemicals** react together to make **new chemicals**.

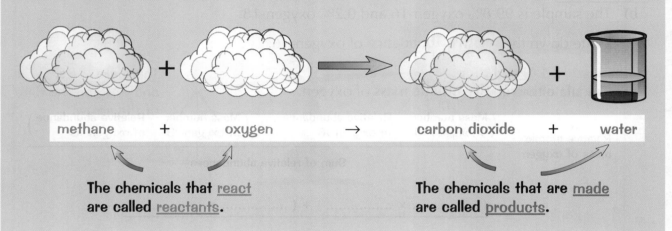

2) For example, when methane and oxygen react you get carbon dioxide and water.

| methane | + | oxygen | → | carbon dioxide | + | water |

The chemicals that <u>react</u> are called <u>reactants</u>.

The chemicals that are <u>made</u> are called <u>products</u>.

3) You can write out a chemical reaction using words or symbols.

4) For example...

methane + oxygen → carbon dioxide + water ⇐ This is called a word equation.

CH_4 + $2O_2$ → CO_2 + $2H_2O$ ⇐ This is called a symbol equation.

reactants   products

Practice Questions

1) What are the reactants in this reaction? hydrogen + oxygen → water

2) What are the products in this reaction? $Na + H_2O → NaOH + H_2$

Section Two — Chemistry

Balancing Equations

Symbol equations **have to show the right numbers of atoms** — they have to be **balanced**.

Balancing Atoms

1) For a **symbol equation** to be right it has to be **balanced**.

2) This means it has to have the **same number** of each type of atom on **each side** of the arrow.

3) You **balance equations** by putting numbers **in front** of the molecules.

Example

$$HCl + Mg \rightarrow MgCl_2 + H_2$$

There's **1 H, 1 Cl** and **1 Mg** on the left of the arrow.

There are **2 Hs, 2 Cls** and **1 Mg** on the right of the arrow.

The equation is **not** balanced. There aren't enough **Hs** or **Cls** on the left.

To **balance** the equation, put a **2** in front of the HCl.

$$\mathbf{2}HCl + Mg \rightarrow MgCl_2 + H_2$$

There are **2 Hs, 2 Cls** and **1 Mg** on the left of the arrow.

There are **2 Hs, 2 Cls** and **1 Mg** on the right of the arrow.

The equation is now **balanced** — there are the **same number** of each type of atom on **each side** of the arrow.

Practice Questions

1) Is this equation balanced? $H_2 + O_2 \rightarrow H_2O$

2) Is this equation balanced? $2H_2 + O_2 \rightarrow 2H_2O$

Equations Questions

Q1   Name the **reactants** and the **products** in the reactions below.

a) nitrogen + hydrogen → ammonia

Reactants: ....

Product: ....

b) lithium + water → lithium hydroxide + hydrogen

Reactants: ....

Products: ....

c) methane + oxygen → carbon dioxide + water

Reactants: ....

Products: ....

Q2   Write a **word equation** for the reaction below.

> **Magnesium reacts with oxygen. Magnesium oxide is made.**

Word equation: ....

Q3   Copper oxide (CuO) reacts with hydrochloric acid (HCl).
Copper chloride ($CuCl_2$) and water (H_2O) are made.

What is the symbol equation for this reaction? Circle the right answer.

$$CuO + 2HCl \rightarrow CuCl_2 + H_2O$$

$$CuCl_2 + 2HCl \rightarrow CuO + H_2O$$

Section Two — Chemistry

Balancing Equations Questions

Q1 This is the **equation** for burning hydrogen in air:

$$2H_2 + O_2 \rightarrow 2H_2O$$

a) How many H and O atoms are shown on the **left-hand** side of the equation?

H ....   O ....

b) How many H and O atoms are shown on the **right-hand** side of the equation?

H ....   O ....

c) Is this equation balanced?

....

Q2 Tick the boxes to show which of the equations below are **balanced** and which are **not balanced**.

		Balanced	Not balanced
a)	$H_2 + Cl_2 \rightarrow 2HCl$	☐	☐
b)	$CuO + HCl \rightarrow CuCl_2 + H_2O$	☐	☐
c)	$N_2 + H_2 \rightarrow NH_3$	☐	☐
d)	$CuO + H_2 \rightarrow Cu + H_2O$	☐	☐
e)	$CaCO_3 \rightarrow CaO + CO_2$	☐	☐

$$Fe_2O_3 + 3CO \rightarrow 2Fe + 3CO_2$$

Hazard Symbols, Acids and Bases

You'll see hazard symbols all the time in the lab — learn what they mean.

Hazard Symbols

1) Some chemical containers have hazard symbols.

2) These tell you how the chemical is dangerous.

 Toxic
Can cause death, for example if you swallow it or breathe it in.

 Harmful
Like toxic but not quite as dangerous.

 Corrosive
Damages living tissues, for example, eyes and skin.

 Highly Flammable
Catches fire easily.

 Irritant
Can cause a nasty red rash or blisters.

Acids and Bases

1) The pH number of a chemical tells you if it's an acid, a base, or neutral.

2) An acid has a pH of less than 7.

3) A base has a pH of greater than 7. An alkali is a base that dissolves in water.

4) Chemicals with a pH of exactly 7 are neutral.

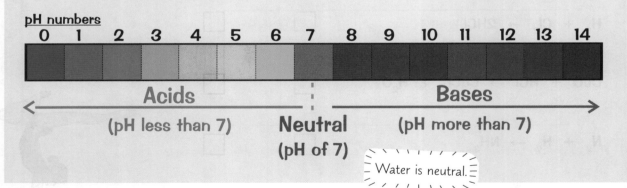

pH numbers
0 1 2 3 4 5 6 7 8 9 10 11 12 13 14

Acids (pH less than 7) Neutral (pH of 7) Bases (pH more than 7)

Water is neutral.

Practice Questions

1) What does this hazard symbol mean?

2) Is the pH number of a base more or less than 7?

3) What is an alkali?

pH and Neutralisation

You can use indicators to find out if something is an acid, a base or neutral.

Indicators

1) An indicator is a dye that changes colour when you put it in an acid or a base.

2) Universal indicator solution gives the colours shown below:

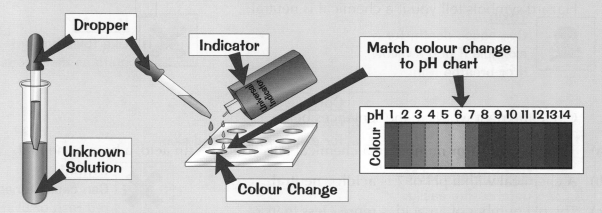

3) Litmus paper is another indicator. It only tells you whether a liquid is an acid or a base — it does not tell you the pH.

Chemical Reactions

1) Chemicals react with each other to form products with different properties.

2) For example, this is what happens when you react an acid with an alkali:

acid + alkali → a salt + water

Salts aren't always like the salt you put on chips.

3) The salt and water are neutral. So it's called a neutralisation reaction.

Practice Questions

1) What is an indicator?

2) Universal indicator turns red when added to a solution. Is the solution an acid or a base?

3) What two things are made when you react an acid with an alkali?

Hazard Symbols, Acids and Bases Questions

Q1   What are **hazard symbols**? Tick the box next to the answer.

Hazard symbols tell you the name of the chemical. ☐

Hazard symbols tell you how much of the chemical to use. ☐

Hazard symbols tell you how a chemical is dangerous. ☐

Hazard symbols tell you if a chemical is neutral. ☐

Q2   Circle the right words in the sentences below.

a)   The **pH** / **indicator** number of a chemical tells you if it's an acid, a base or neutral.

b)   A chemical with a pH of 7 is **acidic** / **neutral**.

c)   The pH number of an acid is **more** / **less** than 7.

Q3   Here is a list of **chemicals** and their **pH numbers**.

Fill in the gap for each chemical by writing if it's an **acid**, a **base** or **neutral**.

		pH Number	Acid, Base or Neutral
a)	Lemon juice	4	....
b)	Pure water	7	....
c)	Soap	11	....
d)	Vinegar	3	....
e)	Baking soda	9	....

pH and Neutralisation Questions

Q1 Are the sentences **true** or **false**? Tick the boxes.

True False

a) Indicators change colour when you put them in an acid or a base. ☐ ☐

b) Universal indicator can turn a range of colours depending on the pH of the solution you put it in. ☐ ☐

c) Litmus paper can tell you the exact pH of a solution. ☐ ☐

Q2 Draw lines to join up the **pH numbers** with the **colours**. One has been done for you.

pH Number   **Colour with Universal Indicator**

pH 2   Green

pH 7   Yellow

pH 12   Red

pH 6   Purple

Q3 Complete the **equation** below. Use words from the list.

Water   Alkali   Salt

Acid + ... → .... + ...

Challenge Yourself

Q4 Robert wants to know the pH of a solution.
Should he use universal indicator or litmus paper?

....

Explain your answer.

....

....

Acid and Metal Reactions

Reactions of Acids with Metals

1) Metals react with acids to give salts and hydrogen:

$$\text{Acid + Metal} \rightarrow \text{Salt + Hydrogen}$$

2) The more reactive the metal, the faster the reaction will go.

3) The rate of reaction is shown by how fast the bubbles of hydrogen are given off.

4) You can test for hydrogen using the burning splint test. It will give a 'squeaky pop'.

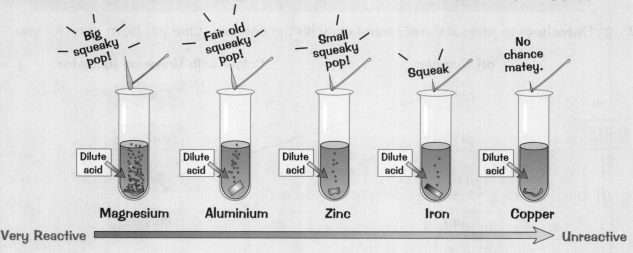

Big squeaky pop!   Fair old squeaky pop!   Small squeaky pop!   Squeak   No chance matey.

Dilute acid   Dilute acid   Dilute acid   Dilute acid   Dilute acid

Magnesium   **Aluminium**   **Zinc**   **Iron**   **Copper**

Very Reactive ———————————————————————→ Unreactive

Salts

1) The metal and acid decide what the salt will be.

2) Hydrochloric acid will always make chloride salts:

> hydrochloric acid + magnesium → magnesium chloride + hydrogen
> hydrochloric acid + aluminium → aluminium chloride + hydrogen

3) Sulfuric acid will always make sulfate salts:

> sulfuric acid + magnesium → magnesium sulfate + hydrogen
> sulfuric acid + aluminium → aluminium sulfate + hydrogen

Come on big guy. I'm going to turn you into salt.

Practice Questions

1) True or false: Acid + Metal → Salt + Oxygen

2) How can you test for hydrogen?

3) What type of salts are made when sulfuric acid reacts with a metal?

Metal Oxides and Metal Hydroxides

Reactions of Metal Oxides and Metal Hydroxides

1) Metal oxides and metal hydroxides are usually alkalis.

2) This means they can react with acids to make a salt and water.

> **Reminder**
> An alkali is a base that dissolves in water.

> **Acid + Metal Oxide → Salt + Water**

> **Acid + Metal Hydroxide → Salt + Water**

3) These are neutralisation reactions.

Salts

1) The metal and acid decide what the salt will be.

2) Hydrochloric acid gives a salt called a chloride:

> hydrochloric acid + copper oxide → copper chloride + water
> hydrochloric acid + zinc oxide → zinc chloride + water
> hydrochloric acid + sodium hydroxide → sodium chloride + water

3) Sulfuric acid gives a salt called a sulfate:

> sulfuric acid + copper oxide → copper sulfate + water
> sulfuric acid + zinc oxide → zinc sulfate + water
> sulfuric acid + sodium hydroxide → sodium sulfate + water

4) Nitric acid gives a salt called a nitrate:

> nitric acid + copper oxide → copper nitrate + water
> nitric acid + zinc oxide → zinc nitrate + water
> nitric acid + sodium hydroxide → sodium nitrate + water

Practice Questions

1) What is made when an acid reacts with a metal hydroxide?

2) Complete this equation: hydrochloric acid + zinc oxide → .... + ...

3) What type of salts are made when nitric acid reacts with a metal hydroxide?

Acid and Metal Reactions Questions

Q1 What is the equation for the reaction of an acid with a metal? Circle the answer.

Acid + Metal → Alkali + Water

Acid + Metal → Salt + Hydrogen

Acid + Metal → Alkali + Hydrogen

Acid + Metal → Salt + Water

Q2 Are the sentences **true** or **false**? Tick the boxes.

True False

a) The more reactive the metal, the slower the reaction will go. ☐ ☐

b) Bubbles of hydrogen are given off in an acid and metal reaction. ☐ ☐

c) A burning splint will go out if hydrogen is present. ☐ ☐

Q3 Draw lines to join up the **reactants** with the **products**.

Reactants

Hydrochloric acid + Copper

Sulfuric acid + Zinc

Hydrochloric acid + Magnesium

Sulfuric acid + Aluminium

Products

Aluminium sulfate + Hydrogen

Zinc sulfate + Hydrogen

Magnesium chloride + Hydrogen

Copper chloride + Hydrogen

Challenge Yourself

Q4 Describe a test that you could use to find out if hydrogen is being given off during a reaction.

....

....

....

Section Two — Chemistry

Metal Oxides and Metal Hydroxides Questions

Q1   Fill in the gaps in the sentences below. Use the words in the boxes.

| sulfate | nitrate | chloride |

a) Hydrochloric acid always gives .... salts.

b) Sulfuric acid always gives .... salts.

c) Nitric acid always gives .... salts.

Q2   Complete the **word equation** below.

> acid + metal hydroxide → salt + ...

Q3   Draw lines to match the reaction to the salt that's made.

Reaction   **Salt**

| hydrochloric acid + copper oxide | | potassium nitrate |

| nitric acid + potassium hydroxide | | copper chloride |

Q4   Write **word equations** for the reactions. Use the chemicals below.

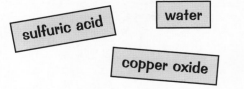

sulfuric acid   water   hydrochloric acid   sodium chloride

copper oxide   copper sulfate   water   sodium hydroxide

a) The reaction between **hydrochloric acid** and **sodium hydroxide**.

....

b) The reaction between **sulfuric acid** and **copper oxide**.

....

Acid and Metal Carbonate Reactions

Reactions of Acids with Metal Carbonates

1) When acids react with metal carbonates you get a salt, water and carbon dioxide.

Acid + Metal Carbonate → Salt + Water + Carbon Dioxide

2) This is a neutralisation reaction.

3) Limewater can be used to test for carbon dioxide.

4) The limewater goes cloudy if there's carbon dioxide there.

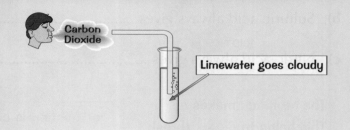

Salts

1) The metal carbonate and acid decide what the salt will be.

2) Hydrochloric acid gives a salt called a chloride:

> hydrochloric acid + sodium carbonate → sodium chloride + water + carbon dioxide
> hydrochloric acid + calcium carbonate → calcium chloride + water + carbon dioxide

3) Sulfuric acid gives a salt called a sulfate:

> sulfuric acid + copper carbonate → copper sulfate + water + carbon dioxide
> sulfuric acid + sodium carbonate → sodium sulfate + water + carbon dioxide

4) Nitric acid gives a salt called a nitrate:

> nitric acid + copper carbonate → copper nitrate + water + carbon dioxide
> nitric acid + calcium carbonate → calcium nitrate + water + carbon dioxide

Practice Questions

1) What is made when an acid reacts with a metal carbonate?

2) What happens when carbon dioxide is bubbled through limewater?

3) What reacts with copper carbonate to produce copper nitrate, water and carbon dioxide?

Uses of Neutralisation Reactions

Neutralisation reactions are pretty useful. We use them for loads of different things.

Indigestion Tablets

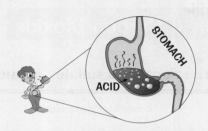 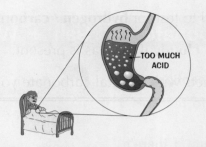 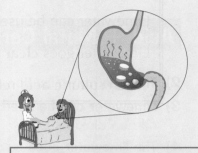

The stomach makes acid. This helps to digest (break down) food and kill bacteria.

Indigestion is caused by too much acid in the stomach.

Indigestion tablets contain a base. They neutralise the extra acid.

1) The base in some indigestion tablets is calcium carbonate.

2) Calcium carbonate is a good base to use because it doesn't dissolve in water.

3) This means that taking too many indigestion tablets isn't likely to be harmful.

Neutralising Acidic Soils

1) Some soils are too acidic for plants to grow in.

2) Adding some base to the soil neutralises the acid.

3) Farmers use calcium oxide to neutralise acidic soils in their fields.

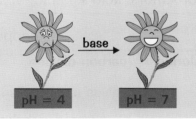

Reducing the Acidity of Lakes

1) Acid rain can cause lakes to become too acidic.

2) This can harm the animals and plants that live in the lake.

3) You can neutralise the acid by adding a base to the lake (for example, calcium carbonate).

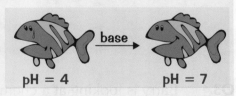

Practice Questions

1) Name a base that is used in indigestion tablets.

2) Why are neutralisation reactions important for farmers?

3) What could cause a lake to become too acidic?

Acid and Metal Carbonate Reactions Questions

Q1   Circle the right words to complete the sentences below.

> When an acid and a metal carbonate react it is **a neutralisation** / **an indicator** reaction.
>
> Limewater can be used to test for **hydrogen** / **carbon dioxide**.
>
> Limewater goes **clear** / **cloudy** if this gas is present.
>
> When sulfuric acid reacts with a metal carbonate you get a salt called a **sulfate** / **nitrate**.

Q2   The reactions below show **acids** reacting with **metal carbonates**.
Finish the word equations. Use **all** the words below each reaction.

a)   sulfuric acid + calcium carbonate →

.... sulfate + ... + ...

carbon dioxide   water   calcium

b)   hydrochloric acid + ... carbonate →

copper .... + water + ...

chloride   carbon dioxide   copper

c)   .... acid + sodium .... →

.... nitrate + water + carbon dioxide

sodium   nitric   carbonate

Q3   Barry is looking at a chemical reaction between sulfuric acid and sodium carbonate.
Are the following sentences true or false?

		True	False
a)	A salt called a chloride is made in the reaction.	☐	☐
b)	Sodium sulfate is made in the reaction.	☐	☐
c)	Carbon dioxide is made in the reaction.	☐	☐
d)	Water is not made in the reaction.	☐	☐

Section Two — Chemistry

Uses of Neutralisation Reactions Questions

Q1 Circle the right words in the sentences below.

> The stomach makes acid to help **digest** / **smell** food.
>
> Having acid in the stomach also helps to **make** / **kill** bacteria.
>
> Indigestion is caused by having **too little** / **too much** acid in the stomach.
>
> Indigestion tablets have **an acid** / **a base** in them.
>
> Indigestion tablets **neutralise the acid** / **make the acid stronger**.

Q2 Are the following sentences **true** or **false**? Tick the boxes.

	True	False
a) Calcium carbonate is used in some indigestion tablets.	☐	☐
b) Plants need the soil to be very acidic to grow well.	☐	☐
c) Acid rain can cause lakes to become too acidic.	☐	☐
d) If lakes are too acidic it could harm the plants and animals in the lake.	☐	☐
e) The acidity of a lake can be decreased by adding acid to it.	☐	☐

Challenge Yourself

Q3 Farmer Jim's crops are not growing well. He thinks the soil might be too acidic. What could he do to improve the growth of his crops?

....

....

....

Types of Energy

Types of Energy and Their Uses

Type of energy	Description	Example of uses
Electrical	From electric current.	Televisions
Light	From the Sun and light bulbs.	Seeing at night
Sound	From things that make noise.	Speakers
Kinetic (Movement)	Anything that's moving has it.	Cars
Nuclear	From nuclear reactions.	Nuclear power stations
Thermal (Heat)	From hot objects.	Cooking food
Gravitational Potential	Anything that can fall has it.	Roller coasters
Elastic Potential	In stretched springs, elastic and rubber bands.	Sling shots
Chemical	In foods, fuels and batteries.	Batteries

Kinetic, gravitational potential and elastic potential are types of mechanical energy.

Storing Energy

Some types of energy can be stored.

Examples:
1) Chemical energy is stored in foods and fuels.
2) Kinetic energy is stored in moving objects.
3) Gravitational potential energy is stored in an object by lifting it up.
4) Elastic potential energy is stored by stretching or squashing a spring.
5) Thermal energy is stored in hot things.
6) Nuclear energy is stored in nuclear fuels.

Practice Questions

1) True or false: all types of energy can be stored.

2) What two types of energy are involved when something is falling?

Energy Transfers

Conservation of Energy

1) Energy can't be created.

2) Energy can't be destroyed.

3) You can only change energy from one type to another.

4) A neat way of saying this is that energy is conserved.

Remember, thermal energy and heat energy are the same thing.

Electrical Devices

Electrical devices transform (change) electrical energy into other types of energy.

Example: Television

A television transforms electrical energy into light energy, sound energy and a bit of heat energy.

Electrical Energy → Light + Sound + Heat Energy

Energy Transfer by Force

When a force moves an object through a distance, energy is transferred.

Example: A Crane Lifting an Object

Chemical energy → Kinetic energy → Gravitational Potential energy

- Chemical energy: The energy stored in the fuel used by the crane.
- Kinetic energy: The crane applies a force to make the object move.
- Gravitational Potential energy: The object gets lifted up.

Practice Questions

1) True or false: when a force moves an object through a distance, energy is created.

2) What does a television transform electrical energy into?

Types of Energy Questions

Q1   Draw lines to match each **type** of energy to its description.
One has been done for you.

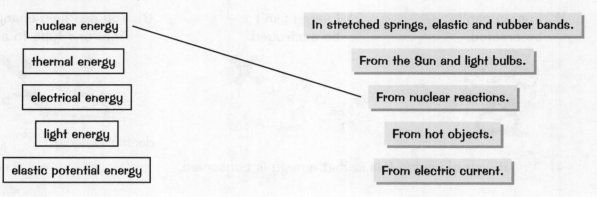

nuclear energy

thermal energy

electrical energy

light energy

elastic potential energy

In stretched springs, elastic and rubber bands.

From the Sun and light bulbs.

From nuclear reactions.

From hot objects.

From electric current.

Q2   Circle the right **types of energy** to answer the questions below.

a)   Bruce eats breakfast. What type of energy is in his **food**?

   Nuclear   **Sound**   **Chemical**

b)   Bruce climbs a tree. What type of energy does he have **at the top of the tree**?

   Gravitational Potential   **Electrical**   **Elastic Potential**

c)   Bruce goes for a drive in a car. What type of energy does he have when **moving**?

   Light   **Kinetic**   **Nuclear**

d)   Bruce **sings** a song. What kind of energy does he give out?

   Chemical   **Gravitational Potential**   **Sound**

Q3   How could you store gravitational potential energy in an object?

....

Energy Transfers Questions

Q1 Are these sentences **true** or **false**? Tick the boxes.

	True	False
a) Energy can be created.	☐	☐
b) Energy can be destroyed.	☐	☐
c) Energy can be transferred from one form to another.	☐	☐
d) Energy is always conserved.	☐	☐

Q2 Complete the following **energy transfers**. One has been done for you.

CD player

Electrical Energy ⟹ Sound Energy + Heat Energy + Light Energy

a) Electric cooker

.... Energy ⟹ Heat Energy + Light Energy

b) Speakers

Electrical Energy ⟹ .... Energy + Heat Energy

c) Laptop screen

Electrical Energy ⟹ .... Energy + ... Energy

Q3 Charlie is pushing an object.

Complete the sentences to describe the energy transfers that are taking place. Use words from the box.

force	chemical	kinetic

Charlie eats food, which contains .... energy.

He uses the energy in the food to apply a .... to the object.

This makes the object move — it gives it .... energy.

More Energy Transfers

Heat energy is transferred from one place to another when there is a difference in temperature.

Heat Energy Transfer — Conduction

1) The particles in hot parts of a solid have more energy and move more.

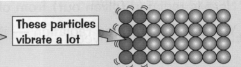

These particles vibrate a lot

hot part of solid   cold part of solid

2) These particles will bang into the particles next to them. They will transfer (pass on) some of their energy to them.

hot   cold

3) This is how heat energy travels through a solid. This is called conduction.

4) Conduction only happens in solids.

5) Metals are good conductors. They transfer heat energy quickly.

Heat Energy Transfer — Convection

Convection is where particles move from a hot place to a cooler one.
It can only happen in liquids and gases. Liquids and gases are both types of fluid.

1) In a colder fluid, particles are closer together. This means cold fluids have a high density.

2) In a hotter fluid, the particles have more energy and are further apart. This means hot fluids have a low density.

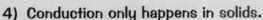
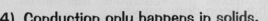

3) Hotter, less dense fluids will move above colder, denser fluids. This is called convection.

4) Convection is how radiators spread warm air around a room:

1 The warmer air rises above the colder, denser air.

Radiator heats air next to it

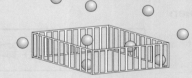

2 As the warm air rises, cooler air falls and takes its place.

3 This carries on so you have air flowing in a circle. This is called a convection current. This is how heat energy is transferred to the whole room.

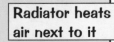

More Energy Transfers

Heat Energy Transfer — Radiation

1) Heat is radiated (given out) from objects as infrared radiation (see p. 104).

2) You can feel infrared radiation — it's hot.

infrared radiation

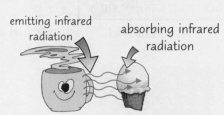

emitting infrared radiation

absorbing infrared radiation

Objects can emit (give out) and absorb (take in) heat radiation.

Hotter objects emit more heat radiation. This makes their temperature fall.

Cooler objects absorb heat radiation. This makes their temperature rise.

Transfer of Sound Energy

1) Sound energy can be transferred from one place to another.

2) It is radiated (given out) as a sound wave from something making a noise.

3) The sound waves cause vibrations in the material they travel in.

4) The vibrations are passed on by particles.

5) So sound energy needs particles to travel.

Vibrations ↔ of particles

Direction of sound wave

Practice Questions

1) True or false: heat flows by convection in solids.

2) True or false: convection only happens in gases.

3) What type of energy is radiated as infrared radiation?

4) What type of wave is given out by something that is making a noise?

More Energy Transfers Questions

Q1 Draw lines to match the type of heat transfer with how it works.

| Conduction | | Particles pass on energy to the particles next to them. |

| Convection | | Particles move from a hot place to a cooler one. |

Q2 Which tank has the higher density of fish? Circle the answer.

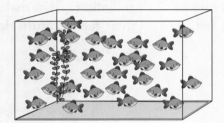 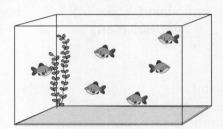

Q3 Are these sentences **true** or **false**? Tick the boxes.

                                                       True False

a) A denser fluid will rise above a less dense fluid. ☐ ☐

b) Hot fluids rise above cold fluids. ☐ ☐

c) Convection can happen in water, but not in air. ☐ ☐

Q4 Radiators can heat up a room by **convection**.

Complete the sentences to explain how this works.
Use words from the box.

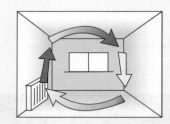

| sinks | energy | rises | hot air |

The air particles near the radiator are heated up and gain ....

The hot air ....

The cool air ....

The cool air fills the gap left by the ....

More Energy Transfers Questions

Q5 **Convection** makes water move inside a water heater.

Draw **arrows** on the diagram to show which way the water moves.

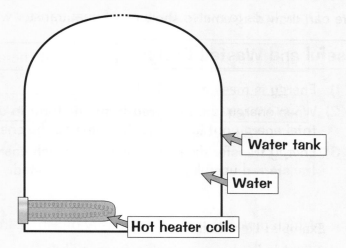

Water tank

Water

Hot heater coils

Q6 Circle the correct words in the sentences below.

a) Infrared radiation is **heat / sound** energy.

b) Hot objects **emit / don't emit** infrared radiation.

c) The **hotter / colder** the object, the more infrared radiation it will emit.

Q7 Which of the sentences below is **true**? Tick one box.

☐ Sound energy is transferred by conduction.

☐ Sound waves pick up vibrations as they travel.

☐ Sound waves cause vibrations in the material they travel in.

Challenge Yourself

Q8 Space doesn't contain any particles.
Sound energy cannot travel through space. Explain why.

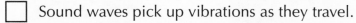

....

Energy and Calculations

We can draw diagrams to show energy transfers.

Useful and Wasted Energy

1) Energy is measured in Joules (J).

2) When energy is transferred from one form to another the total energy out is always the same as the energy put in.

3) Energy transfer diagrams show how much energy is transferred usefully and how much is wasted.

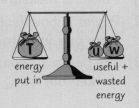

energy put in | useful + wasted energy

Example: Light bulb

A light bulb changes electrical energy into useful light energy and wasted heat energy.

Here's the energy transfer diagram for a light bulb:

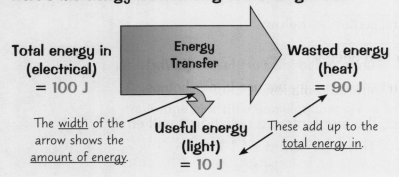

Total energy in (electrical) = 100 J

Energy Transfer

Wasted energy (heat) = 90 J

The <u>width</u> of the arrow shows the <u>amount of energy</u>.

Useful energy (light) = 10 J

These add up to the <u>total energy in</u>.

Reminder
Energy is conserved — it can't be created or destroyed.

Wasted energy is dissipated. This means it is spread out and lost to the surroundings.

Calculating Efficiency

Efficiency is the proportion (amount) of the energy in that is transferred into useful energy:

$$\text{Efficiency} = \frac{\text{Useful Energy}}{\text{Total Energy Supplied}} \times 100\%$$

The more efficient something is, the less energy it wastes.

Example: Kettle

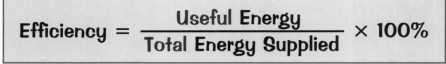

180 000 J of electrical energy in

9000 J of <u>wasted</u> heat (to the room)

171 000 J of <u>useful</u> heat (to the water)

1) The total energy supplied is the amount of energy going in = 180 000 J

2) The useful energy is the energy being used to heat the water = 171 000 J.

Efficiency = 171 000 ÷ 180 000 × 100%
Efficiency = 95%.

Always give efficiency as a percentage (%).

Energy and Calculations

Calculating Power

1) Power is measured in watts (W).

2) Power is how fast energy is transferred from one form to another.

3) The power of something can be worked out using this equation:

$$\text{Power (in watts, W)} = \frac{\text{Energy (in joules, J)}}{\text{Time (in seconds, s)}}$$

Example: A machine transfers 200 J in 10 seconds. What is the power of the machine?

Answer: Power = Energy ÷ Time = 200 ÷ 10 = 20 W

Calculating the Cost of Electricity

1) Electricity can be measured in units called kilowatt-hours (kWhr).

2) We have to pay for every unit of electricity we use in our homes.

3) You can work out the cost of using an appliance with this equation:

$$\text{Cost} = \underset{\text{(in kW)}}{\text{Power}} \times \underset{\text{(in hours)}}{\text{Time}} \times \underset{\text{(in pence)}}{\text{Cost of 1 kWhr}}$$

Example: Electricity costs 10p per kWhr.
Find the cost of leaving a 1500 W tumble dryer on for 3 hours.

Answer: First, change the units of power to kW:
1000 W = 1 kW, so 1500 W = 1500 ÷ 1000 = 1.5 kW

There are 1000 W in a kW.

Then use the equation to find the cost:
Cost = Power × Time × Cost of 1 kWhr
= 1.5 kW × 3 h × 10p = 45p

Practice Questions

1) True or false: efficiency is the proportion of the energy that is wasted.

2) What is the efficiency of a light bulb that transfers 100 J of electrical energy into 10 J of useful light energy?

3) Bob's electricity costs 15p per kWhr. Work out how much it costs him to use a 0.1 kW bulb for 4 hours.

Energy and Calculations Questions

Q1 Are the sentences **true** or **false**? Tick the boxes.

True False

a) Efficiency is the share of the energy put in that is transferred into useful energy. ☐ ☐

b) Energy transferred that's not useful is called wasted energy. ☐ ☐

c) The more efficient a light bulb is, the more energy it wastes. ☐ ☐

d) Energy is measured in watts (W). ☐ ☐

Q2 Draw lines to match each object with its **useful energy change**.
One has been done for you.

Object:

car

light bulb

iron

Useful energy change:

electrical ⟹ heat

chemical ⟹ kinetic

electrical ⟹ light

Q3 Here is an **energy transfer diagram** for an electric lamp.
Complete the sentences below. Use the diagram to help.

energy in
100 J

light energy
out 5 J

heat energy
out

a) The total energy in is .... J

b) The amount of useful energy is .... J

c) The amount of energy wasted is .... J

Q4 A kettle has a power of **2 kW**.

a) What is its power in **watts**? Tick the box next to the right answer.

☐ 2 W   ☐ 200 W   ☐ 2000 W

b) The kettle runs off electricity from the mains supply.
What **units** is this electricity measured in?

☐ kilowatt-hours   ☐ watts   ☐ joules

Energy and Calculations Questions

Q5 a) Complete the **efficiency** formula below. Use words from the list.

total energy supplied   efficiency   useful energy

$$\text{.........................} = \frac{\text{...}}{\text{...}} \times 100\%$$

b) Use the **efficiency formula** to complete the table below. One has been done for you.

Total Energy Supplied (J)	Useful Energy (J)	Efficiency (%)
200	20	10
4000	2000	
4000	1000	

Q6 The **power** of an appliance is how much electricity it uses over a certain time.

a) A hair dryer uses **120 000 J** of energy in **120 seconds**.
Complete the calculation to find the power of the hair dryer.

Power (W)   =   Energy (J)   ÷   Time (s)

=   ....   ÷   ....

=   .... W

b) Write down the power of the hair dryer in **kW**.

....

Q7 An electricity company charges **7 pence per kilowatt-hour**.
Calculate how much it costs to leave a **0.5 kW** washing machine on for **2 hours**.

Cost of energy   =   power   ×   time   ×   cost of 1 kilowatt-hour

=   ....   ×   ....   ×   7p

=   .... p

Renewable Energy Sources 1

The energy from renewable energy sources can be transformed into electrical energy.

What are Renewable Energy Sources?

1) A renewable energy source is one that will never run out.
2) But they don't give out as much energy as the non-renewables (see page 96).
3) The renewables are hydroelectricity, wave power, tidal power, wind power, solar power, geothermal energy and biofuels.

Hydroelectricity

Hydroelectricity uses water stored behind a dam:

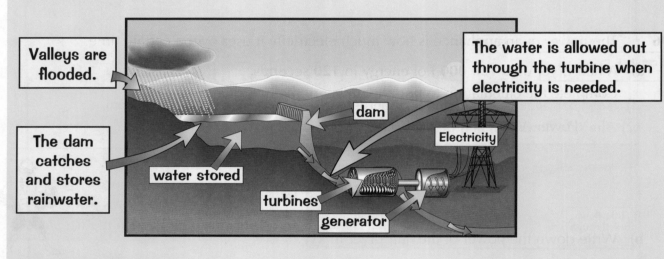

Valleys are flooded.

The dam catches and stores rainwater.

The water is allowed out through the turbine when electricity is needed.

dam

Electricity

water stored

turbines

generator

Energy transfers:

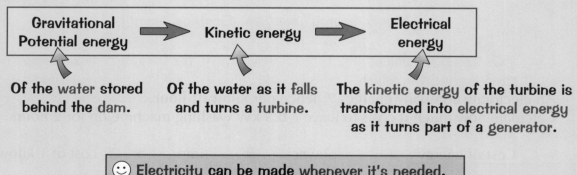

Gravitational Potential energy → Kinetic energy → Electrical energy

Of the water stored behind the dam.

Of the water as it falls and turns a turbine.

The kinetic energy of the turbine is transformed into electrical energy as it turns part of a generator.

☺ Electricity can be made whenever it's needed.
☹ Building a dam is very expensive.

Renewable Energy Sources 1

Wave Power

Waves move up and down, which turns a turbine:

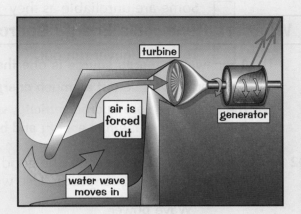

😊	It's useful on small islands.
☹	It's unreliable because waves aren't as big when the wind drops.
☹	It doesn't give much energy.

Energy transfers:

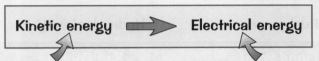

Kinetic energy ➡ Electrical energy

Of the waves which forces air to turn a turbine and a generator.

The generator transforms the kinetic energy into electrical energy.

Tidal Power

1) Tidal barrages are big dams built across rivers. They have turbines in them.
2) The tide flowing in and out turns the turbines.

😊	It gives loads of energy.
😊	It's very reliable because tides happen every day.
☹	It can only be used in certain places.

Energy transfers:

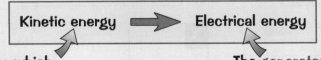

Kinetic energy ➡ Electrical energy

Of the water which turns the turbine, which turns a generator.

The generator transforms the kinetic energy into electrical energy.

Practice Questions

1) True or false: renewable energy sources will never run out.

2) Give one advantage of using hydroelectric power to generate electricity.

3) What type of energy is transformed into electrical energy in a tidal barrage?

Renewable Energy Sources 1 Questions

Q1   Tick **one** box to show a **good** point of renewable energy sources.

☐ Some are unreliable as they depend on the weather.

☐ Many can only be used in certain places.

☐ They will never run out.

☐ They don't give out as much energy as non-renewables.

Q2   Complete the table to show the good and bad points of **renewable energy sources**. Use words from the list.

Wave power   Tidal power   Hydroelectricity

Renewable source	Good Point	Bad Point
	Useful on small islands.	Won't work when the wind drops.
	Very reliable.	Can only be used in certain places.
	Electricity can be made whenever it's needed.	Building a dam is very expensive.

Q3   Add the labels to the diagram to show how **wave power** works.
Write the correct letters in the boxes.

A — water wave moves in

B — turbine turns generator to make electricity

C — air turns turbine

D — air is forced out

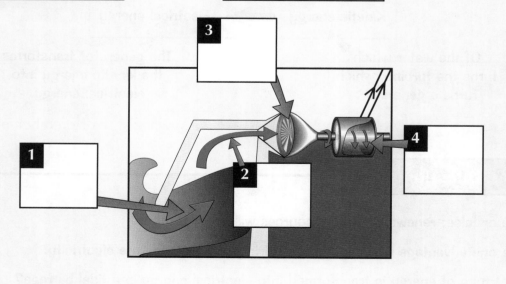

Renewable Energy Sources 1 Questions

Q4 Complete the labels on the diagram of a **hydroelectric power station**.
Use sentences from the box.

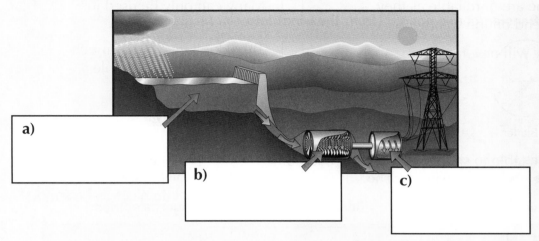

The turbine turns a generator to produce electricity.

Water is let out through the turbine.

A dam catches and stores rain water.

a)

b)

c)

Q5 Are these sentences describing **hydroelectricity**, **tidal** power or **both**? Tick the boxes.

	Hydroelectricity	Tidal	Both
a) It is usually used across rivers.	☐	☐	☐
b) Kinetic energy is transformed into electrical energy.	☐	☐	☐
c) It can provide electricity when you need it.	☐	☐	☐

Q6 Circle the correct words in the sentences below.

a) Waves have **kinetic / heat** energy which is used to turn a turbine.

b) Wave power is useful **on small islands / near rivers**.

c) Wave power is **reliable / unreliable** because it depends on the weather.

d) Wave power **does / doesn't** produce a lot of energy.

Challenge Yourself

Q7 Describe the **energy transformations** that take place when water stored behind a dam is used to make electricity in a **hydroelectric power station**.

....

....

....

Section Three — Physics

Renewable Energy Sources 2

Wind Power

Wind turbines **transfer** kinetic energy (from the wind) into electrical energy.

Blades

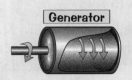
Generator

1) The wind has **kinetic energy**. It turns the **blades** of a wind turbine.

2) The blades turn a **generator** inside the turbine, which transforms the **kinetic energy** into **electrical energy**.

Energy transfers:

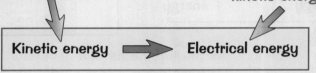
Kinetic energy ➤ Electrical energy

☺ They can be used on a **small** or **large scale**.

☺ They're useful in **remote places** (where you might not be able to get mains electricity).

☹ They **only** work when it's **windy**.

Using on a large scale means having lots in one place.

Solar Cells

Solar cells **transform** light energy from the Sun into electrical energy.

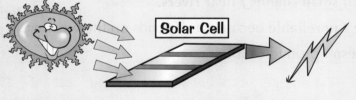
Solar Cell

A solar panel is made up of lots of solar cells.

Energy transfers:

Light energy ➤ Electrical energy

☺ They're **reliable** in sunny places in the **daytime**.

☺ They can be used on a **small** or **large scale**.

☺ They're useful in **remote places**.

☹ They **don't** work at **night** or when it's **cloudy**.

Renewable Energy Sources 2

Geothermal Energy

Geothermal energy is heat from underground.

☺ It's cheap to run.

☹ You can only use it where hot rocks are near the surface. There are not many places you can do it.

Water is pumped down to hot rocks underground.

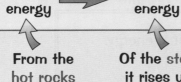

It comes back up as steam to drive a turbine.

Energy transfers:

Heat energy → Kinetic energy → Electrical energy

From the hot rocks underground.

Of the steam as it rises up and turns the turbine.

As the turbine turns a generator it transforms kinetic energy to electrical energy.

Biofuels

1) Biofuels are made from plants.
2) Biofuels are burnt to heat up water to make steam.
3) The steam drives a turbine:

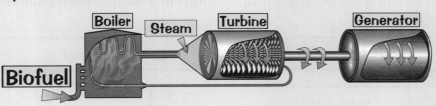

Plants   Biofuel

☺ Biofuels are quick and cheap to make.

☹ Lots of land is needed to grow the plants for biofuels.

Energy transfers:

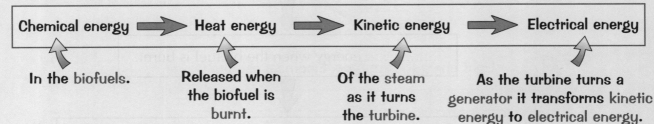

Chemical energy → Heat energy → Kinetic energy → Electrical energy

In the biofuels.

Released when the biofuel is burnt.

Of the steam as it turns the turbine.

As the turbine turns a generator it transforms kinetic energy to electrical energy.

Practice Questions

1) True or false: wind turbines only generate electricity when it is needed.

2) What type of energy do solar cells convert into electrical energy?

3) Give one disadvantage of using geothermal energy.

Renewable Energy Sources 2 Questions

Q1   Are the sentences **true** or **false**? Tick the boxes.

True False

a)   Wind turbines transform the kinetic energy of the wind into electrical energy.   ☐ ☐

b)   Wind power can be used on a large scale.   ☐ ☐

c)   Wind turbines generate power whatever the weather.   ☐ ☐

Q2   Circle the right words to complete the sentences on **solar cells**.

> Solar cells transform **light / kinetic** energy into electrical energy.
>
> They are very **reliable / unreliable** in sunny places.
>
> They are often used in very **remote / crowded** places like mountains.
>
> They don't work **at night / during the day** or when it's cloudy.

Q3   Complete the flow chart showing the energy transformations in a **biofuel** power station. Use words from the box below.

| heat | electrical | kinetic | chemical |

.... energy in the biofuel.

⬇

.... energy when the biofuel is burnt.

⬇

.... energy of the steam produced by heating the water, and of the turbine as the steam turns it.

⬇

.... energy produced by the turbine turning the generator.

Renewable Energy Sources 2 Questions

Q4   Draw lines to match each renewable energy source with its **energy transformations**.

| Geothermal Energy |

| Wind Power |

| Solar Power |

Kinetic Energy ➤ Electrical Energy

Light Energy ➤ Electrical Energy

Heat Energy ➤ Kinetic Energy ➤ Electrical Energy

Q5   Use the words to fill in the gaps in the sentences.

turbine   **generator**   **water**

Biofuels are burnt to heat .... to make steam.

This steam is used to drive a ....

This then turns a ....

Challenge Yourself

Q6   Give **one** advantage and **one** disadvantage of using **biofuels**.

Advantage: ....

....

Disadvantage: ....

....

Non-Renewable Energy Sources

What are Non-Renewable Energy Sources?

1) Non-renewable energy sources are ones that will run out at some point.

2) The non-renewables are:

| Fossil fuels | Nuclear fuels |

(oil, coal and natural gas)

Fossil Fuel Power Stations

1) Most of the electricity we use is generated (made) from fossil fuels in power stations.

2) Coal, oil and natural gas are burnt to heat water.

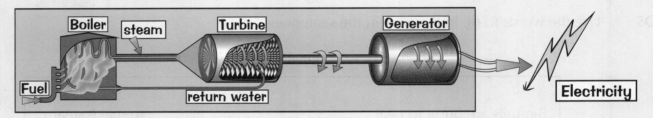

Energy transfers:

Chemical energy ➡ Heat energy ➡ Kinetic energy ➡ Electrical energy

| Stored in the fuel. | Released from the fuel and turns water to steam. | Of the steam. The steam turns a turbine, which turns a generator. | The generator transforms kinetic energy to electrical energy. |

Nuclear Power Stations

1) Nuclear power stations work in a similar way to fossil fuel power stations.

2) The only difference is the heat energy comes from a nuclear reaction.

Energy transfers:

Nuclear energy ➡ Heat energy ➡ Kinetic energy ➡ Electrical energy

| Stored in the fuel. | Released from the fuel and turns water to steam. | Of the steam. The steam turns a turbine, which turns a generator. | The generator transforms kinetic energy to electrical energy. |

Non-Renewable Energy Sources

Advantages of Non-Renewable Energy Sources

1) Fossil fuels give out a lot of energy and nuclear fuels give out even more.

2) All the fuels are pretty cheap.

3) We can rely on them to provide us with electricity when we need it.

Disadvantages of Non-Renewable Energy Sources

1) Non-renewable energy sources will run out.

2) They can harm the environment.

Batteries and Fuel Cells

1) Batteries and fuel cells store energy.

2) They transform chemical energy into electrical energy:

Chemical energy  Electrical energy

3) Batteries and fuel cells are useful when you can't get mains electricity or other sources of electricity.

4) Batteries are portable (they can be carried around).

5) But batteries and fuel cells can be more expensive to use than other energy sources.

Practice Questions

1) Will non-renewable energy sources run out?

2) How are coal, oil and natural gas used to heat water in a power station?

3) Give two advantages of using non-renewables.

Non-Renewable Energy Sources Questions

Q1   Complete the sentences below using words from the box.

burnt	reactions	fossil

a) Coal, oil and gas are .... fuels.

They are .... to make heat.

b) Nuclear .... in nuclear fuels release heat.

Q2   Are these sentences **true** or **false**? Tick the boxes.

                                                                    True   False

a) Coal and gas are both non-renewable energy sources.   ☐   ☐

b) Non-renewable energy sources will never run out.   ☐   ☐

c) Nuclear fuels are a renewable energy source.   ☐   ☐

d) Chemical energy is stored in fossil fuels.   ☐   ☐

Q3   Add the labels to the diagram of a **fossil fuel** power station
by writing the correct letters in the boxes.

A — Boiler	B — Generator	C — Steam	D — Turbine	E — Fuel

water

1   2   3   4   5

Non-Renewable Energy Sources Questions

Q4 Which of the sentences below is **true**? Tick **one** box.

[ ] Fossil fuels don't give out much energy.

[ ] Fossil fuels are very expensive to buy.

[ ] Fossil fuels are an unreliable source of energy.

[ ] Non-renewable energy sources can harm the environment.

Q5 Circle the right words to complete the sentences on **batteries** and **fuel cells**.

> Batteries transform **nuclear / chemical** energy to electrical energy.
>
> Fuel cells are useful when you **can / can't** get mains electricity.
>
> Batteries **are / aren't** useful in a hand-held device.
>
> Fuel cells can be **a cheap / an expensive** source of energy.

Q6 Complete the flow chart showing the energy transformations in a **nuclear power station**. Use words from the box below.

heat	electrical	kinetic	nuclear

.... energy in the fuel.

⬇

.... energy released during nuclear reactions.

⬇

.... energy of the steam produced by heating water, and of a turbine as the steam turns it.

⬇

.... energy produced by the turbine turning a generator.

Wave Basics

You have to know what all the words to do with waves mean.

The Parts of a Wave

1) Waves transfer (move) energy from place to place.

2) All waves have amplitude, wavelength and frequency.

3) Below is a diagram of a wave:

Amplitude

1) This is the distance from the mid-point to a peak or trough.

2) Amplitude is measured in metres (m).

Wavelength

1) This is the length of a full cycle of the wave.

2) For example, measuring the distance from peak to peak gives you the wavelength.

3) Wavelength is measured in metres (m).

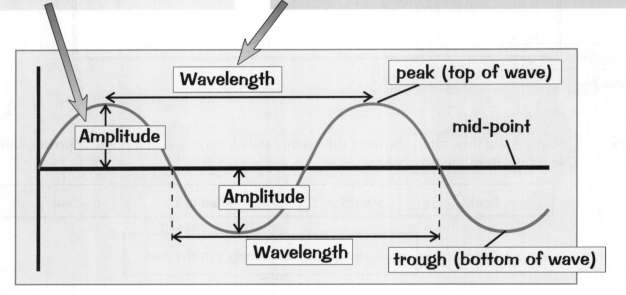

Frequency

1) This is how many whole waves pass a certain point every second...

2) ... or the number of waves made each second.

3) Frequency is measured in hertz (Hz).

4) 1 Hz is 1 wave per second.

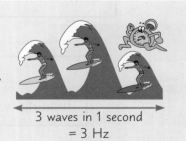

3 waves in 1 second
= 3 Hz

Wave Basics

Wave Speed

1) **Wave speed** is the speed that a wave is travelling at.

2) It's measured in **metres per second (m/s)**.

3) This equation lets you work out the **speed of a wave:**

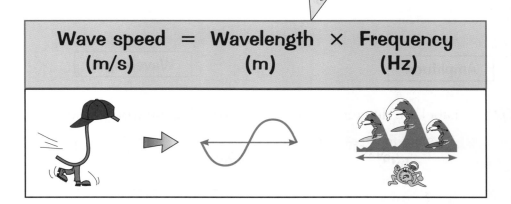

$$\text{Wave speed} \atop \text{(m/s)} = \text{Wavelength} \atop \text{(m)} \times \text{Frequency} \atop \text{(Hz)}$$

Standard Form

1) **Standard form** is a way of writing very **big** or **small** numbers.

2) For example, 6.4×10^4 is the same as **64 000**.

3) To type 6.4×10^4 into a **calculator**, you would press: 6 • 4 EXP 4

Example: A wave has a frequency of 6.4×10^4 Hz.
Its wavelength is 0.1 m. What is its speed?

Answer: Speed = wavelength × frequency
= 0.1 m × 6.4×10^4 Hz
= 6400 m/s (= 6.4×10^3 m/s)

Practice Questions

1) True or false: waves transfer energy.

2) What is frequency measured in?

3) What is the amplitude of a wave?

4) What is the wavelength of a wave?

5) A wave has a frequency of 1.6×10^4 Hz and a wavelength of 0.2 m. Find its speed.

Wave Basics Questions

Q1 Are the sentences **true** or **false**? Tick the boxes.

True False

a) Waves transfer energy from one place to another. ☐ ☐

b) Amplitude is measured in hertz (Hz). ☐ ☐

c) 1 Hz is 10 waves per second. ☐ ☐

d) To find the wavelength of a wave, measure the distance from peak to trough. ☐ ☐

Q2 Label the different parts of the wave using the words below.

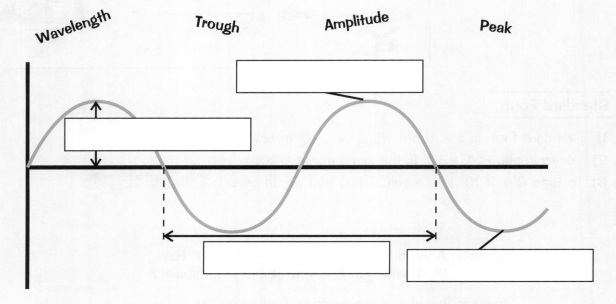

Wavelength   Trough   Amplitude   Peak

Q3 Draw lines to match the words with their descriptions.

Wavelength		How many waves pass a certain point every second.
Frequency		The distance from the mid-point to a peak or a trough.
Amplitude		The length of a full cycle of a wave.

Wave Basics Questions

Q4 Diagrams **A**, **B** and **C** are pictures of waves.

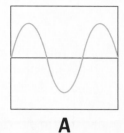 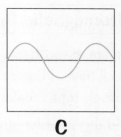

A **B** **C**

a) Which two diagrams show waves with the same **amplitude**? .... and ....

b) Which two diagrams show waves with the same **wavelength**? .... and ....

Q5 A **sound wave** has a wavelength of **4 m** and a frequency of **85 Hz**.
Calculate the **speed** of the sound wave.

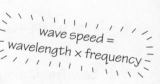
wave speed = wavelength × frequency

....

.... m/s

Q6 A **water wave** has a frequency of **2.5 Hz** and a wavelength of **1.2 m**.

Tick the box next to the **speed** of the water wave.

3 m/s ☐   0.48 m/s ☐

3.7 m/s ☐   2.08 Hz ☐

Q7 A wave has a wavelength of **10 m** and a frequency of **3.2 × 10⁶ Hz**.
Complete the calculation to find the speed of the wave.

wave speed = wavelength × frequency

wave speed = ... × ....

wave speed = ... m/s

Uses of Electromagnetic Waves 1

Electromagnetic (e.m.) waves are really useful to us. Here is more about them...

The Electromagnetic Spectrum

1) There are seven types of electromagnetic wave.

2) They all have different wavelengths and frequencies.

3) The seven types make up the electromagnetic spectrum:

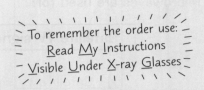

To remember the order use:
Read My Instructions
Visible Under X-ray Glasses

Radio waves	Micro-waves	Infra-red	Visible Light	Ultra-violet	X-rays	Gamma Rays

Long wavelength ⟵ **Decreasing Wavelength** ⟶ Short wavelength

Low frequency ⟵ **Increasing Frequency** ⟶ High frequency

4) The electromagnetic spectrum is continuous (there are no gaps between groups).

5) Each group has a range of wavelengths.
For example, not all radio waves have the same wavelength (see below).

Uses of Radio Waves

Broadcasting means sending out to a large area.

1) Radio waves are used for:
   • broadcasting TV and radio signals.
   • transmitting (sending) satellite signals.

2) Different wavelengths of radio wave are used for the different things:

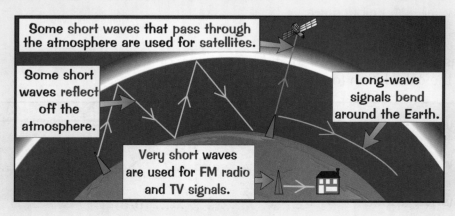

Some short waves that pass through the atmosphere are used for satellites.

Some short waves reflect off the atmosphere.

Long-wave signals bend around the Earth.

Very short waves are used for FM radio and TV signals.

Uses of Electromagnetic Waves 1

Uses of Microwaves

Microwaves are used for:

Satellite TV signals

1) Satellite TV signals **travel as microwaves** from a transmitter to a satellite in space.

2) **The satellite sends it to your satellite TV dish.**

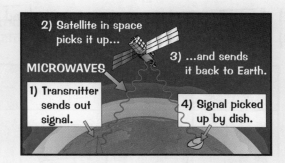

2) Satellite in space picks it up...

MICROWAVES

3) ...and sends it back to Earth.

1) Transmitter sends out signal.

4) Signal picked up by dish.

Mobile phone signals

Mobile phone signals **travel as microwaves between your phone** and the nearest transmitter.

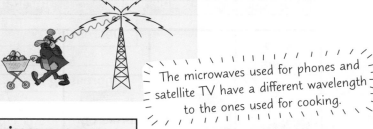

The microwaves used for phones and satellite TV have a different wavelength to the ones used for cooking.

Cooking in microwave ovens

1) **Water in food absorbs energy** from microwaves.

2) This heats the water and cooks the food.

Weather forecasting

1) Microwaves are **reflected** by rain drops.

2) So microwaves can be used to work out:
   - how **far away** clouds are
   - how **fast** clouds are moving

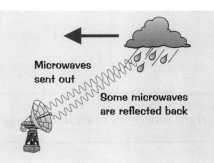

Microwaves sent out

Some microwaves are reflected back

Practice Questions

1) How many types of electromagnetic wave are there?

2) Give one use of radio waves.

3) Give two uses of microwaves.

Uses of Electromagnetic Waves 1 Questions

Q1 Circle **two** uses of **radio waves** below.

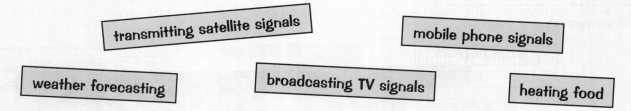

transmitting satellite signals

mobile phone signals

weather forecasting

broadcasting TV signals

heating food

Q2 a) Complete the electromagnetic spectrum using words from the box.

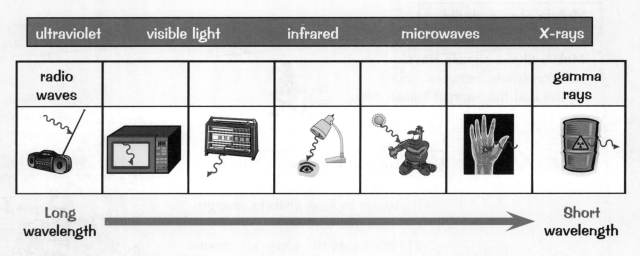

| ultraviolet | visible light | infrared | microwaves | X-rays |

radio waves						gamma rays

Long wavelength →→→ Short wavelength

b) Which type of electromagnetic radiation has the **lowest frequency**?

....

Q3 Circle the right words to complete the sentences below.

> Radio waves with **short / long** wavelengths reflect off the Earth's atmosphere.
>
> Radio waves with **short / long** wavelengths can bend around the Earth.
>
> Very **short / long** radio waves are used to transmit TV and FM radio signals.

Section Three — Physics

Uses of Electromagnetic Waves 1 Questions

Q4 Microwaves are used to send **satellite TV signals**.

a) Complete the labels on the diagram to show how this works. Use words from the box.

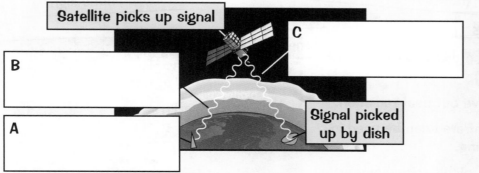

Satellite picks up signal

B

A

C

Signal picked up by dish

Satellite sends signal to Earth

Microwaves

Transmitter sends out signal

b) What other type of communication uses microwaves? Tick the box.

☐ mobile phones

☐ radio signals

☐ landline phones

Q5 Are these sentences **true** or **false**? Tick the boxes.

                                                    True False

a) All electromagnetic waves have the same frequency. ☐ ☐

b) Radio waves have the shortest wavelength of all electromagnetic waves. ☐ ☐

c) Microwaves can be used in weather forecasting. ☐ ☐

d) Gamma rays have a higher frequency than radio waves. ☐ ☐

Q6 Microwaves are used in microwave ovens to **cook** food.

a) What substance in food **absorbs energy** from microwaves? Circle the answer.

carbon   salt   protein   water

Extra Large Popcorn

b) What happens to substances when they absorb microwave energy? Tick one box.

☐ They heat up.

☐ They get charged.

☐ They give out light.

Uses of Electromagnetic Waves 2

Uses of Infrared Radiation

Infrared radiation has loads of uses:

Thermal Imaging

1) Infrared is also called heat radiation (see page 81).

2) All objects give out heat radiation.

3) This means infrared can be used in thermal imaging.

For example, night-vision cameras:

A night-vision camera picks up the infrared and shows it on the screen.

A hidden 'bad guy' gives off infrared.

Optical fibres

1) Optical fibres can carry information over long distances.

2) For example, they are used in telephone cables.

3) The information is sent as pulses of infrared waves:

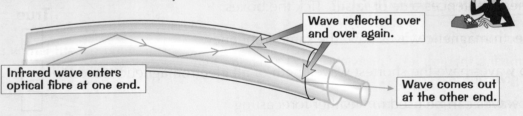

Wave reflected over and over again.

Infrared wave enters optical fibre at one end.

Wave comes out at the other end.

Around the Home

Infrared radiation can also be used in:

Cooking (grills and toasters)

Remote Controls

Radiant Heaters (For example, patio heaters.)

Security Systems (burglar alarms and security lights)

These sensors detect body heat.

Uses of Electromagnetic Waves 2

Uses of Visible Light

1) We need visible light to see.

2) Different wavelengths of visible light are different colours:

Red, Orange, Yellow, Green, Blue, Indigo, Violet

We call this the visible light spectrum.

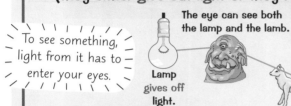

Long wavelength ◀━━ **Decreasing Wavelength** ━━▶ Short wavelength

3) We see objects because they are illuminated (they either give out light or they reflect light).

To see something, light from it has to enter your eyes.

The eye can see both the lamp and the lamb.

Lamp gives off light.

Lamb reflects light.

4) Visible light is used in photography.

Light goes into the camera.

Thing being photographed

Uses of Ultraviolet Radiation

1) Some chemicals are fluorescent.

2) This means they absorb ultraviolet (UV) radiation and then give out visible light.

3) Fluorescent chemicals have many uses:

Fluorescent Lamps

Fluorescent lamps use UV to give out visible light.

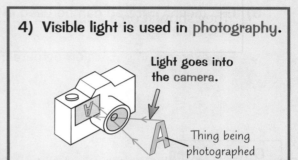

Detecting Forged Bank Notes

- Banks print markings in fluorescent ink on bank notes.
- Under a UV light, real notes will show the fluorescent markings.
- Fake notes just glow, and there are no markings.

Under UV light:

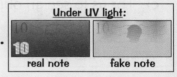

real note · fake note

1) Ultraviolet radiation can disinfect water.

2) It kills any germs in the water to make it safer.

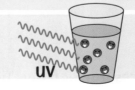

UV

Practice Questions

1) Give two uses of infrared around the home.

2) What type of radiation helps us to see objects?

3) Give one use of ultraviolet radiation.

Uses of Electromagnetic Waves 2 Questions

Q1 Complete the sentences using words from the box.

pick up	thermal	screen

Infrared can be used in .... imaging.

Night-vision cameras .... infrared radiation from hot objects.

They show it on a .... as a picture.

Q2 Complete the sentences about **visible light**.
Use words from the boxes under each sentence.

a) We can see some objects because they .... visible light.

give out	conduct

b) We can see other objects because they .... light.

take in	reflect

c) For us to see an object, light from it needs to enter our ....

mouth	nose	eyes

Q3 Are the sentences **true** or **false**? Tick the boxes.

                                                              True False

a) All colours of visible light have the same wavelength. ☐ ☐

b) Visible light is used in photography. ☐ ☐

c) Fluorescent lamps use visible light to give out ultraviolet (UV) radiation. ☐ ☐

d) Ultraviolet (UV) radiation can be used to disinfect water. ☐ ☐

Uses of Electromagnetic Waves 2 Questions

Q4 Information can be sent through **optical fibres**.

a) Tick the boxes next to the **two** sentences that are **true**.

☐ Optical fibres carry information over long distances.

☐ Optical fibres carry sound waves.

☐ Optical fibres are used in telephone cables.

b) Which type of radiation is used in optical fibres?
Circle **one** answer.

| **Ultraviolet** | **Microwaves** | **Infrared** | **Radio** |

Q5 a) What happens to fluorescent ink when it absorbs **ultraviolet radiation**? Tick the box.

It gives out visible light. ☐

It gives out ultraviolet (UV) radiation. ☐

It gives out X-rays. ☐

b) Circle the right words in the sentences below.

Banks use fluorescent ink when they make **bank notes / coins**.

Under UV lights, real ones show special markings, but fake ones just **glow / burn**.

Challenge Yourself

Q6 Name **three** ways that infrared radiation can be used in the home.

1. ....

2. ....

3. ....

Uses of Electromagnetic Waves 3

Uses of X-rays

1) Medical X-rays are used to look inside people to see if they have any broken bones.

2) Airports use X-ray security scanners to look inside bags for dangerous things.

3) Airports can also use them on passengers to look for things like hidden weapons.

Uses of Gamma Rays

Treating Cancer

Gamma radiation is used to treat cancer:

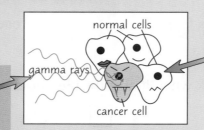

normal cells

gamma rays

cancer cell

The rays are directed carefully at the cancer cells.

They kill the cancer cells without killing too many normal cells.

Detecting Cancer

Gamma rays can also be used to detect (spot) cancer:

radioactive source gives off gamma rays

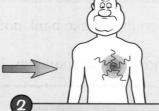

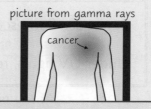

picture from gamma rays

cancer

1 A radioactive source that gives off gamma rays is put into the body.

2 The source travels around the body and ends up where the cancer is.

3 A special camera can be used to detect the gamma rays and find the cancer.

Sterilising Food and Equipment

1) Gamma rays can be used to sterilise food (kill all the germs).

2) This keeps the food fresh for longer.

3) Medical instruments can be sterilised in the same way.

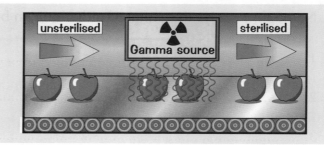

unsterilised

Gamma source

sterilised

Uses of Electromagnetic Waves 3

Electromagnetic radiation is very useful in many ways, but it can be dangerous too.

Harmful Effects of Electromagnetic Radiation

Being exposed to too much radiation can be harmful.

Microwaves

1) Microwaves can heat cells inside the human body.
2) This can damage them.

Cell

Mobile phones use microwaves. Some people worry that they might damage the brain. (But nothing has been proved.)

Infrared

If your body gets too much infrared, it can cause skin burns.

Ultraviolet (UV)

1) When skin cells on the surface absorb UV radiation from the Sun it can cause sunburn.
2) This can cause skin cancer.
3) UV can also damage your eyes.

Gamma and X-rays

1) Gamma rays and X-rays are both very dangerous.
2) They can cause cell damage.
3) They can also cause cell mutation (change), which can lead to cancer.

The danger of e.m. waves increases as their frequency increases.

Practice Questions

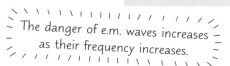

1) What type of electromagnetic wave is used to look inside people for broken bones?

2) Give two uses of gamma rays.

3) True or false: UV radiation can cause skin cancer.

Section Three — Physics

Uses of Electromagnetic Waves 3 Questions

Q1 Complete the sentences about **gamma rays**. Use words from the box.

carefully	kill	cancer	normal

High doses of gamma radiation will .... living cells.

Because of this, gamma radiation is used to treat ....

The gamma rays are .... directed at the cancer cells.

This is so they don't kill too many .... cells.

Q2 Are the sentences **true** or **false**? Tick the boxes.

True False

a) Airport security scanners use X-rays to look inside people's bags. ☐ ☐

b) Gamma rays are used to detect and treat cancer. ☐ ☐

c) X-rays are not harmful to humans. ☐ ☐

d) Infrared radiation can cause skin burns. ☐ ☐

Q3 Number the steps below 1-4 to show how **gamma rays** can be used to **detect** cancer. One has been done for you.

☐ The camera makes a picture which can be used to look for cancer.

1 A radioactive source is put into the patient's body.

☐ A special camera is used to detect the gamma rays emitted from the source.

☐ The source travels around the body.

Uses of Electromagnetic Waves 3 Questions

Q4 Different types of e.m. radiation can cause different **problems**. Put **all** the problems from the box into the table below.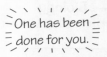

One has been done for you.

> sunburn   heating body cells   skin burns
>
> cell mutation   ~~cancer~~   skin cancer

Type of e.m. Radiation	Problems it can cause
Microwaves	
Infrared	
Ultraviolet	
Gamma / X-rays	cancer

Challenge Yourself

Q5 Explain why it is useful to expose **food** to **gamma rays**.

....

....

....

Answers

Section One — Biology

Page 5

1) genes
2) the cytoplasm
3) Any one from: vacuole / cell wall / chloroplast
4) false — A group of cells come together to make a tissue. / A group of organs work together to form an organ system.

Pages 6-7

1)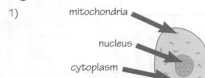
mitochondria
nucleus
cytoplasm
cell membrane

2) Cell membrane — Lets substances in and out of the cell.
Cytoplasm — Where most of the chemical reactions in the cell happen.
Mitochondria — Where respiration happens.
3) a) vacuole
   b) chloroplast
4)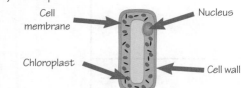
Cell membrane
Nucleus
Chloroplast
Cell wall
5) cell → tissue → organ
6) An organ system

Page 9

1) an electrical signal
2) biconcave
3) To defend the body against disease.
4) So that it can swim and find an egg to fertilise.
5) cytoplasm

Pages 10-11

1) a) a nerve cell
   b) motor neurone
   c)
2) a) neurone
   b) white blood cell
   c) red blood cell
   d) egg cell
3) a) false — White blood cells defend the body against disease.
   b) true
   c) false — Red blood cells have a biconcave shape.
   d) true
4) The following statements are about egg cells:
   They contain genes from the mother.
   They contain cytoplasm.
   They are large and bulky.
5) The tail can move. This allows the sperm cell to swim and find an egg cell.
   The head contains enzymes. These are chemicals that help it get into an egg so the sperm and egg can join.

Page 13

1) glucose
2) Any one from: they take in water from the soil / they stop the plant blowing away or falling over / they provide anchorage.

Pages 14-15

1) a) root hair cell
   b) roots
   c) It takes up water from the soil.
2)

Xylem	Phloem
water minerals	glucose

3) a) Roots
   b) Leaves
   c) Leaves
   d) Roots
4) leaves, stomata, water, water vapour
5) a, b, c)
Y
X
6) Water vapour is lost from the leaves through the stomata. This means there's less water in the leaves, so more water is drawn up the plant through the xylem tubes. This draws water up from the roots.

Page 17

1) Guanine (G)
2) alleles

Pages 18-19

1) a) nucleus
   b) chromosome
   c) gene
2)

A	C	T	G	C	A	A	T	G
T	G	A	C	G	T	T	A	C

3) Heterozygous — Two different alleles.
   Homozygous — Two alleles the same.
   Phenotype — The characteristics that you have.
4) a) nucleus
   b) DNA
   c) genes
5) a) the dominant characteristic
   b) the recessive characteristic
   c) the dominant characteristic
6)

Genotype	Phenotype
RR	Read minds
Rr	Read minds
rr	Control minds

Page 21

1) true
2) blue

Pages 22-23

1) a) false — Sophie and Becky are sisters, but Alyson is the partner of Hector (Sophie and Becky's brother).
   b) Nn
   c) Becky, Ronald
   d) Yes — the baby could have the alleles nn.

Answers

2) a)
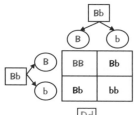

b) Black
c) Black
d) Brown

3) a)
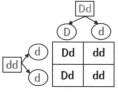

b) Dd — yes
dd — no
c) 50%

Page 25

1) The order of the DNA bases in the gene changes.
2) false — Some mutations can be useful.

Pages 26-27

1) a) false — Mutations can be harmful or useful.
b) false — A mutation is a change in the order of the DNA bases in a gene.
2) new characteristics
3) A
4) A change in the order of the DNA bases in a gene.
5) a) Susan is a carrier.
b) ff
c) no

Page 29

1) sensory neurone, motor neurone
2) by chemicals called neurotransmitters

Pages 30-31

1) a) central nervous system
b) brain, spinal cord
2) Sensory neurones carry impulses from receptors to the CNS.
Motor neurones carry impulses from the CNS to effectors.
3) a) receptor
b) sensory
c) motor
d) effector
4) a) fast
b) hurting
c) without
d) neurones
e) neurotransmitters
5) a) W = synapse, X = synapse, Y = motor neurone
b) effector
6) An electrical impulse travels along a neurone. The electrical impulse reaches the end of the neurone. Neurotransmitters move across the synapse. The neurotransmitters set off a new electrical impulse in the next neurone.

Page 33

1) endocrine glands
2) in the blood
3) false — Hormones carry information slower than nerves.
4) Any one from: insulin / glucagon

Pages 34-35

1) Glands that make hormones.
2) a) false — Hormones are chemicals.
b) true
c) true

d) false — Organs that respond to hormones are called target organs.
3) a) a hormone
b) endocrine system
4)

	Nerves	Hormones
a) Which carries information faster?	✓	
b) Which causes the response which lasts the longest?		✓
c) Which carries information in the blood?		✓

5) a) glucagon
b) insulin
6) a) up
b) insulin
c) down
7) Glucagon is released into the blood. This makes the amount of glucose in the blood go up/back to normal.

Page 37

1) true
2) Body temperature falls.
3) get wider
4) Any two from: it shivers / body hairs stand on end / blood vessels in the skin get narrower.

Pages 38-39

1) a) B — Keeping conditions inside your body the same.
b) Body temperature regulation
c) hormones
2)

Warm Up	Cool Down
shivering	sweating
body hair standing on end	more blood flowing near the surface

3) a) When you're too hot
b) When you're too hot
c) When you're too cold
4) Vasodilation is where blood vessels in the skin get wider. More blood flows near the surface of Bob's skin. This means he can lose more heat.

Section Two — Chemistry

Page 41

1) protons and neutrons
2) positive
3) 4
4) A substance that only has one type of atom.

Pages 42-43

1)
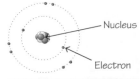
Nucleus
Electron

2)

Part of the atom	Charge
Proton	Positive
Neutron	Neutral
Electron	Negative

3) The nucleus is made up of protons and neutrons.
4) copper and oxygen should be circled

Answers

5) a) 1
   b) 5
   c) 3
   d) 12

Page 45

1) groups
2) periods
3) false — All the elements in a group have the same number of electrons in their outer shells.

Pages 46-47

1) A should be circled
2) a)

   b) 11
3) The total number of protons and neutrons.
4) a) potassium and rubidium should be ticked
   b) electrons, similar
5) You would find which group carbon is in. The group number is the same as the number of electrons in the outer shell of the atom. Carbon's in Group 4 so there will be 4 electrons in the outer shell of the atom.

Page 49

1) true
2) Compounds are substances made when atoms of two or more elements are chemically combined (joined) together.

Pages 50-51

1) CO   OCO   OO
2) CO   OCO
3) a) Two atoms joined together.
   b) A molecule made of two different atoms.
4) a) CO_2
   b) H_2O
   c) H_2O
5) a) O
   b) Mg
   c) Cu
6) a) false — The substance is a compound.
   b) true
   c) false — There is no carbon in the substance, only hydrogen and nitrogen.
   d) true

Page 53

1) the inside shell
2) up to eight
3) 2, 8, 8
4) 2, 8, 1

Pages 54-55

1) a) true
   b) true
2) a) 9
   b)

   c) 1
3) a) 2, 6
   b) 2, 8, 2
   c) 2, 8, 4

4) a) 2, 8, 7
   b)

   c) 2
5) a)

   b)

Page 57

1) Isotopes are atoms of the same element, which have the same number of protons but a different number of neutrons.
2) How much there is of the isotope compared to the total amount of the element in the world.

Pages 58-59

1) neutrons
2) X and Z
3) a) false — The relative atomic mass of an element might not be a whole number, it can be a decimal.
   b) false — Isotopes of the same element have the same numbers of electrons/different numbers of neutrons.
4) a) 16
   b) 99.8%
   c) Relative atomic mass of oxygen = $\dfrac{(16 \times 99.8) + (18 \times 0.2)}{99.8 + 0.2}$
      = 16.0
5) Relative atomic mass of copper = $\dfrac{(63 \times 70) + (65 \times 30)}{70 + 30}$
   = 63.6

Page 60

1) hydrogen and oxygen
2) NaOH and H_2

Page 61

1) no (there aren't enough Os on the right of the arrow)
2) yes

Page 62

1) a) Reactants: nitrogen, hydrogen
      Product: ammonia
   b) Reactants: lithium, water
      Products: lithium hydroxide, hydrogen
   c) Reactants: methane, oxygen
      Products: carbon dioxide, water
2) magnesium + oxygen → magnesium oxide
3) $CuO + 2HCl → CuCl_2 + H_2O$

Page 63

1) a) Number of H atoms: 4
      Number of O atoms: 2
   b) Number of H atoms: 4
      Number of O atoms: 2
   c) Yes
2) a) balanced
   b) not balanced
   c) not balanced
   d) balanced
   e) balanced

Page 64

1) corrosive
2) more than 7
3) A base that dissolves in water.

Answers

Page 65

1) A dye that changes colour when you put it in an acid or a base.
2) an acid
3) a salt and water

Page 66

1) Hazard symbols tell you how a chemical is dangerous.
2) a) pH
   b) neutral
   c) less
3) a) acid
   b) neutral
   c) base
   d) acid
   e) base

Page 67

1) a) true
   b) true
   c) false — Litmus paper only tells you whether a solution is an acid or a base.
2) pH 7 — green
   pH 12 — purple
   pH 6 — yellow
3) Acid + Alkali → Salt + Water
4) Universal indictor. Litmus paper only tells you if a solution is an acid or a base. It doesn't tell you the pH of the solution.

Page 68

1) false — Acid + Metal → Salt + Hydrogen
2) Use a burning splint. It will give a squeaky pop.
3) sulfate salts

Page 69

1) A salt and water.
2) hydrochloric acid + zinc oxide → zinc chloride + water
3) nitrates

Page 70

1) Acid + Metal → Salt + Hydrogen
2) a) false — The more reactive the metal, the faster the reaction will go.
   b) true
   c) false — A burning splint will give a squeaky pop if hydrogen is present.
3) Hydrochloric acid + Copper — Copper chloride + Hydrogen
   Sulfuric acid + Zinc — Zinc sulfate + Hydrogen
   Hydrochloric acid + Magnesium — Magnesium chloride + Hydrogen
   Sulfuric acid + Aluminium — Aluminium sulfate + Hydrogen
4) Put a burning splint near to the reaction. If hydrogen is being given off there will be a squeaky pop.

Page 71

1) a) chloride
   b) sulfate
   c) nitrate
2) water
3) hydrochloric acid + copper oxide — copper chloride
   nitric acid + potassium hydroxide — potassium nitrate
4) a) hydrochloric acid + sodium hydroxide → sodium chloride + water
   b) sulfuric acid + copper oxide → copper sulfate + water

Page 72

1) A salt, water and carbon dioxide.
2) The limewater turns cloudy.
3) nitric acid

Page 73

1) calcium carbonate
2) Neutralisation reactions can be used to neutralise acidic soils.
3) acid rain

Page 74

1) a neutralisation, carbon dioxide, cloudy, sulfate
2) a) sulfuric acid + calcium carbonate →
         calcium sulfate + water + carbon dioxide
   b) hydrochloric acid + copper carbonate →
         copper chloride + water + carbon dioxide
   c) nitric acid + sodium carbonate →
         sodium nitrate + water + carbon dioxide
3) a) false — A salt called a sulfate is made in the reaction.
   b) true
   c) true
   d) false — Water is made in the reaction.

Page 75

1) digest, kill, too much, a base, neutralise the acid
2) a) true
   b) false — Plants will not grow well if the soil is too acidic.
   c) true
   d) true
   e) false — The acidity of a lake can be decreased by adding base to it.
3) He could add some base (e.g. calcium oxide) to the soil to neutralise the acid. This would make the soil less acidic.

Section Three — Physics

Page 76

1) false — Only some types of energy can be stored.
2) gravitational potential and kinetic

Page 77

1) false — When a force moves an object through a distance, energy is transferred.
2) light energy, sound energy and heat/thermal energy

Page 78

1) nuclear energy — From nuclear reactions.
   thermal energy — From hot objects.
   electrical energy — From electric current.
   light energy — From the Sun and light bulbs.
   elastic potential energy — In stretched springs, elastic and rubber bands.
2) a) Chemical
   b) Gravitational Potential
   c) Kinetic
   d) Sound
3) By lifting it up.

Page 79

1) a) false — Energy cannot be created.
   b) false — Energy cannot be destroyed.
   c) true
   d) true
2) a) **Electrical** Energy → Heat Energy + Light Energy
   b) Electrical Energy → **Sound** Energy + Heat Energy
   c) Electrical Energy → **Light** Energy + **Heat/Thermal** Energy
3) chemical, force, kinetic

Answers

Page 81

1) false — Heat flows by conduction in solids.
2) false — Convection happens in both gases and liquids.
3) heat energy
4) sound wave

Pages 82-83

1) Conduction — Particles pass on energy to the particles next to them.
Convection — Particles move from a hot place to a cooler one.

2)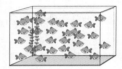

3) a) false — A less dense fluid will rise above a denser fluid.
   b) true
   c) false — Convection can happen in both water and air.
4) energy, rises, sinks, hot air
5)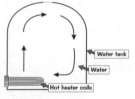

6) a) heat
   b) emit
   c) hotter
7) Sound waves cause vibrations in the material they travel in.
8) Sound needs particles to travel. The particles pass on the vibrations of a sound wave.

Page 85

1) false — Efficiency is the proportion of the energy that is transferred into useful energy.
2) Efficiency = Useful energy ÷ Total energy supplied × 100%
   = 10 J ÷ 100 J × 100% = **10%**
3) Cost = power × time × cost of 1 kWhr
   = 0.1 kW × 4 h × 15p = **6p**

Pages 86-87

1) a) true
   b) true
   c) false — The more efficient a light bulb is, the less energy it wastes.
   d) false — Energy is measured in joules (J).
2) car — chemical → kinetic
   light bulb — electrical → light
   iron — electrical → heat
3) a) 100 J
   b) 5 J
   c) wasted energy = total energy – useful energy
   wasted energy = 100 J – 5 J = 95 J
4) a) 2000 W
   b) kilowatt-hours
5) a) $\text{efficiency} = \dfrac{\text{useful energy}}{\text{total energy supplied}} \times 100\%$
   b)

Total Energy Supplied (J)	Useful Energy (J)	Efficiency (%)
200	20	10
4000	2000	**50**
4000	1000	**25**

6) a) Power = Energy ÷ Time
   = 120 000 J ÷ 120 seconds = **1000 W**
   b) 1000 W = **1 kW**
7) Cost of energy = **0.5 kW × 2 hours × 7p**
   = **7p**

Page 89

1) true
2) Electricity can be made whenever it is needed.
3) kinetic energy

Pages 90-91

1) They will never run out.
2)

Renewable source	Good Point	Bad Point
Wave power	Useful on small islands.	Won't work when the wind drops.
Tidal power	Very reliable.	Can only be used in certain places.
Hydroelectricity	Electricity can be made whenever it's needed.	Building a dam is very expensive.

3) 1 — A
   2 — D
   3 — C
   4 — B
4) a) A dam catches and stores rain water.
   b) Water is let out through the turbine.
   c) The turbine turns a generator to produce electricity.
5) a) Tidal
   b) Both
   c) Hydroelectricity
6) a) kinetic
   b) on small islands
   c) unreliable
   d) doesn't
7) Gravitational potential energy of the water stored behind the dam is transformed into kinetic energy as the water falls. The water turns the turbine, which turns a generator and transforms the kinetic energy into electrical energy.

Page 93

1) false — Wind turbines generate electricity when it is windy.
2) light energy
3) You can only use it where hot rocks are near the ground's surface. This means there are not many places you can do it.

Pages 94-95

1) a) true
   b) true
   c) false — Wind turbines only generate power when it is windy.
2) light, reliable, remote, at night
3) chemical, heat, kinetic, electrical
4) geothermal energy — heat energy → kinetic energy → electrical energy
   wind power — kinetic energy → electrical energy
   solar power — light energy → electrical energy
5) water, turbine, generator
6) Advantage: Biofuels are quick and cheap to make.
   Disadvantage: Lots of land is needed to grow the plants to make biofuels.

Page 97

1) yes
2) They are burnt.
3) Any two from: They give out a lot of energy. / All the fuels are pretty cheap. / We can rely on them to provide us with electricity when we need it.

Pages 98-99

1) a) fossil, burnt
   b) reactions

Answers

2) a) true
   b) false — Non-renewable energy sources will run out.
   c) false — Nuclear fuels are a non-renewable energy source.
   d) true
3) 1 — E
   2 — A
   3 — C
   4 — D
   5 — B
4) Non-renewable energy sources can harm the environment.
5) chemical, can't, are, an expensive
6) nuclear, heat, kinetic, electrical

Page 101

1) true
2) hertz (Hz)
3) The distance from the mid-point of a wave to a peak or trough.
4) The length of a full cycle of a wave.
5) wave speed = wavelength × frequency
   = 0.2 m × 1.6 × 10^4 Hz = 3200 m/s (= 3.2 × 10^3 m/s)

Pages 102-103

1) a) true
   b) false — Amplitude is measured in metres (m).
   c) false — 1 Hz is 1 wave per second.
   d) false — To find the wavelength of a wave, measure the distance from peak to peak (or trough to trough, or mid-point to mid-point).

2)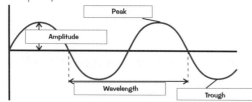

3) Wavelength — The length of a full cycle of a wave.
   Frequency — How many waves pass a certain point every second.
   Amplitude — The distance from the mid-point to a peak or trough.
4) a) A and B
   b) A and C
5) wave speed = wavelength × frequency
   = 4 × 85 = 340 m/s
6) wave speed = wavelength × frequency
   = 1.2 × 2.5 = 3 m/s
7) wave speed = wavelength × frequency
   = 10 × 3.2 × 10^6
   = 3.2 × 10^7 m/s (= 32 000 000 m/s)

Page 105

1) 7
2) Any one from: broadcasting TV and radio signals / transmitting satellite signals
3) Any two from: satellite TV signals / mobile phone signals / cooking / weather forecasting

Pages 106-107

1) broadcasting TV signals, transmitting satellite signals
2) a)

radio waves	micro-waves	infrared	visible light	ultraviolet	X-rays	gamma rays

   b) radio waves
3) short, long, short

4) a) A — Transmitter sends out signal
      B — Microwaves
      C — Satellite sends signal to Earth
   b) mobile phones
5) a) false — Electromagnetic waves can have different frequencies.
   b) false — They have the longest wavelength.
   c) true
   d) true
6) a) water
   b) They heat up.

Page 109

1) Any two from: cooking / remote controls / security systems / radiant heaters
2) visible light
3) Any one from: fluorescent lamps / detecting forged bank notes / disinfecting water

Pages 110-111

1) thermal, pick up, screen
2) a) give out
   b) reflect
   c) eyes
3) a) false — Different colours of visible light have different wavelengths.
   b) true
   c) false — Fluorescent lamps use UV radiation to give out visible light.
   d) true
4) a) Optical fibres carry information over long distances. Optical fibres are used in telephone cables.
   b) Infrared
5) a) It gives out visible light.
   b) bank notes, glow
6) Any three from: grills / toasters / remote controls / security systems / burglar alarms / security lights / radiant heaters.

Page 113

1) X-rays
2) Any two from: treating cancer / detecting cancer / sterilising food / sterilising medical instruments
3) true

Pages 114-115

1) kill, cancer, carefully, normal
2) a) true
   b) true
   c) false — X-rays are harmful to humans.
   d) true
3) 1 — A radioactive source is put into the patient's body.
   2 — The source travels around the body.
   3 — A special camera is used to detect the gamma rays emitted from the source.
   4 — The camera makes a picture which can be used to look for cancer.
4)

Type of EM Radiation	Problems it can cause
Microwaves	heating body cells
Infrared	skin burns
Ultraviolet	skin cancer sunburn
Gamma / X-rays	cancer cell mutation

5) Gamma rays kill germs. So exposing food to gamma rays is a way of sterilising it. This means food will stay fresh for longer.

Glossary

acid	A chemical with a pH of less than 7.
alkali	A base that dissolves in water.
allele	A version of a gene.
amplitude	The distance from the mid-point of a wave to a peak or trough (measured in m).
atomic number	The number of protons in an atom.
base	A chemical with a pH of more than 7.
cardiovascular system	An organ system made up of the heart and blood vessels.
chloroplast	The part of a plant cell where photosynthesis happens.
chromosome	A very long bit of DNA found in the nucleus of a cell.
compound	A substance where atoms of two or more elements are chemically combined together.
conduction	The transfer of heat energy through a solid.
conservation of energy	Energy cannot be created or destroyed, only changed from one type to another.
continuous	Something with no gaps.
convection	The transfer of heat energy through fluids (gases and liquids).
convection current	A circular flow of liquid or gas that happens because of convection.
cytoplasm	The part of a cell where most of the chemical reactions happen.
DNA	A double helix (double-stranded spiral) made up of genes which control characteristics.
effector	A cell or organ which brings about a response to a stimulus.
efficiency	The proportion (amount) of the energy in that is transferred into useful energy.
electromagnetic spectrum	A continuous spectrum made up by the 7 types of electromagnetic wave (radio waves, microwaves, infrared, visible light, ultraviolet, X-rays and gamma rays).
electron	A negatively charged particle in an atom.
electronic configuration	The number of electrons in each shell of an atom.
element	A substance made up of only one type of atom.

Glossary

energy transfer	When energy is moved from one place to another.
energy transfer diagrams	Diagrams to show how much energy is transferred usefully and how much is wasted.
energy transformation	When energy is changed from one type to another type.
fluid	A liquid or a gas.
fossil fuels	Coal, oil and natural gas.
frequency	How many whole waves pass a certain point every second, or how many waves are made every second.
gene	A short section of DNA which controls a characteristic.
genotype	The alleles you have. For example, Bb.
group	A column in the periodic table.
hazard symbol	A symbol on a chemical container that tells you how the chemical is dangerous.
hertz (Hz)	The unit of frequency (1 Hz = 1 wave per second).
heterozygous	Where you have two different alleles for a characteristic.
homeostasis	Keeps the conditions inside your body the same.
homozygous	Where you have two alleles which are the same for a characteristic.
hormone	Chemicals made by glands in the body.
indicator	A dye that changes colour when you put it in an acid or a base.
indigestion	When you have too much stomach acid.
infrared radiation	Heat given out by hot objects and part of the electromagnetic spectrum.
isotope	Atoms of the same element, which have the same number of protons but a different number of neutrons.
joules (J)	The unit of energy.
kilowatt-hour (kWhr)	A unit of electricity.
mass number	The total number of protons and neutrons in an atom.
mitochondria	The part of a cell where respiration happens.

Glossary

mixture	A mix of substances that are not chemically joined up.
molecule	Formed when atoms join together.
motor neurone	A nerve cell. It carries electrical impulses from the CNS to effectors.
mutation	A change in the order of the DNA bases in a gene.
neurone	A nerve cell. These cells carry information to and from the central nervous system.
neurotransmitter	A chemical which moves across a synapse.
neutralisation	When an acid reacts with an alkali or base to form a neutral solution.
neutron	A particle in an atom that has no charge.
non-renewable energy source	An energy source that will eventually run out (e.g. fossil fuels, nuclear fuels).
nucleus (biology)	The part of a cell that contains genes.
nucleus (chemistry)	Protons and neutrons in the centre of an atom.
organ	A group of different tissues which work together.
organ system	A group of organs which work together.
peak	The top of a wave.
period	A row in the periodic table.
periodic table	A table used by scientists to organise all of the elements.
phenotype	The characteristics you have. For example, brown eyes.
phloem	Tubes made up of phloem cells. The tubes carry glucose up and down a plant's stem.
pH number	A number which tells you if a chemical is an acid, a base or neutral.
power	How fast energy is transferred from one form to another.
proton	A positively charged particle in an atom.
receptor	A group of cells that detect a stimulus.
reflex	An automatic response to a stimulus.
relative abundance	How much there is of an isotope compared to the total amount of the element in the world.

Glossary

renewable energy source	An energy source that will never run out (e.g. solar, wind, hydroelectric power).
root hair cell	A 'hair-like' cell found on a plant's roots. It absorbs water from the soil.
salt	A chemical formed in a neutralisation reaction.
sensory neurone	A nerve cell. It carries electrical impulses from receptors to the CNS.
shell	A layer of electrons in an atom.
sound wave	How sound energy is transferred from one place to another.
standard form	A way to write very big or very small numbers. For example, 6.4×10^4 Hz.
stimulus	A change in your environment.
synapse	A tiny gap between neurones.
tissue	A group of similar cells.
transpiration	The loss of water from a plant's leaves.
trough	The bottom of a wave.
vacuole	A large space in a plant cell filled with cell sap. It helps the cell keep its shape.
watts (W)	The unit of power.
wavelength	The length of a full cycle of a wave (measured in m).
wave speed	The speed that a wave is travelling at (measured in m/s).
xylem	Tubes made up of xylem cells. The tubes carry water and minerals from the roots to the leaves in a plant.

Index